BIOLOGY
· PRINCIPLES & EXPLORATIONS ·

Active Reading Guide
with Answer Key

HOLT, RINEHART AND WINSTON

A Harcourt Classroom Education Company

Austin · New York · Orlando · Atlanta · San Francisco · Boston · Dallas · Toronto · London

To the Teacher

The Active Reading Guide worksheets serve to develop students' reading skills. Students will use their comprehension, decoding, and vocabulary skills to identify and note relationships among words. Each worksheet contained in the guide correlates to a specific section of the textbook. Passages and illustrations have been taken directly from the textbook. Completion of the worksheets serves to reinforce both students' reading skills and their understanding of core biology content. A four-page introduction appears on pages vii–x. An answer key can be found at the back of this book.

Writer
Theresa Flynn-Nason
Science Teacher
Voorhees Public Schools
Voorhees, NJ

Illustration Credits: Page 13, Kristy Sprott; 37, Rosiland Solomon; 49, Kristy Sprott; 73, Morgan-Cain & Associates; 77, Kristy Sprott; 84, Uhl Studios, Inc.; 99, Rosiland Solomon; 112, Rosiland Solomon; 124, Pond Giles; 131, Rosiland Solomon; 133, Rosiland Solomon; 143, Morgan-Cain & Associates; 166, Keith Kasnot; 168, Thomas Gagliano; 171, Thomas Gagliano; 174, Thomas Gagliano; 181, Thomas Gagliano.

Printed in the United States of America

ISBN 0-03-055322-9

1 2 3 4 5 6 7 8 9   18   05 04 03 02 01 00

Table of Contents

v

Using the Active Reading Guide

The Active Reading Guide serves to develop and reinforce students' reading skills to simplify the ease with which they learn biology. Each worksheet contained in the guide correlates to a specific section of the *Biology: Principles and Explorations* Pupil's Edition. The passages and illustrations, which form the basis of each worksheet, are summaries of passages from the textbook. Abbreviated passages may be used to tie previously-mentioned concepts to the current concept. Completion of the worksheets serves to reinforce both students' reading skills and their understanding of core biology content.

Reading Skills

There are many different types of printed matter, each with its own unique personality. As a result, the reading skills used to gain meaning from science text generally differ from those skills used when reading texts from other disciplines. The Active Reading Guide was designed to highlight the skills that facilitate understanding of science text. Labels on each Active Reading Guide worksheet note the skill that is emphasized. These six skills are:

- **Sequencing Information** Science text commonly includes descriptions of complex processes broken down into a series of sequential steps. Recognition of this text structure is sparked by identification of clue words such as *first, initially, then, before, after, next,* and *finally*. If readers approach a passage knowing it uses a sequential text structure, they are likely to derive meaning from text. An example from the worksheets is shown below.

SKILL: Sequencing Information

Complete each statement by writing the correct number in the space provided. Write *1* if the phrase describes the first trophic level, write *2* if the phrase describes the second trophic level, or write *3* if the phrase describes the third trophic level.

a. _____ Primary consumers are found here.

b. _____ Organisms here use the energy of the sun to build energy-rich carbohydrates.

c. _____ Tigers, wolves, and snakes are found here.

d. _____ Organisms here are capable of breaking down cellulose.

- **Recognizing Similarities and Differences** Science text often introduces new concepts by comparing and contrasting the ideas with previously explored topics. Certain clue words, such as *like, similarly, unlike, however,* and *differ* indicate this text structure. Graphic organizers, such as concept maps, flow charts, and Venn diagrams, also focus the reader's attention on the similarities and differences that exist among topics. Prior knowledge of these structures helps a reader gain meaning quickly and easily.

- **Interpreting Graphics** A graphic is any type of visual that communicates information to an observer. Gaining meaning from a graphic is dependent upon recognition of basic structures such as its title, labels, and key.

- **Organizing Information** Tables, charts, and graphic organizers are three devices commonly used to organize information. Realizing the significance of titles, headings, and symbols helps the reader recognize the structure of such organizers and gain meaning from them.

SKILL: Organizing Information

The figure below shows a Punnett square. The Punnett square shows a cross between two pea plants that are heterozygous for seed color. Use the Punnett square to answer the questions that follow. Write your answers in the spaces provided.

Yy
(Heterozygous)

Box 1	*Yy*
Yy	Box 4

Yy
(Heterozygous)

a. What pair of letters should appear in Box 1?

_____

b. What pair of letters should appear in Box 4?

_____

c. How many homozygous dominant offspring would be produced?

_____

- **Reading Effectively** In order to receive a message from printed matter, the reader must identify words and note relationships among those words. Several vocabulary and comprehension skills are involved in this complex process. An effective reader draws upon such vocabulary and decoding skills as identifying key terms, using context clues to determine meanings of unknown words, and using knowledge of word parts such as prefixes and suffixes to define terms. Once words have been identified, the reader draws upon comprehension skills to weave meanings of isolated terms into complete thoughts and ideas. Such comprehension skills include identifying the main idea of a passage, noting supporting details, and drawing conclusions.

- **Recognizing Cause and Effect** Another text structure used to convey scientific information is cause and effect. A cause and effect relationship defines how two seemingly isolated events are linked. The first event to occur, or the cause, triggers a second event, or effect, to happen. Effective readers understand that certain clue words, such as *since, because,* and *due to,* generally precede a cause. They also recognize that other clue words, such as *consequently, as a result,* and *therefore,* often precede an effect. An example from the worksheets is shown below.

SKILL: Recognizing Cause and Effect

Two independent events can be linked in a cause-and-effect relationship. The first event to occur, or the cause, triggers a second event, or the effect, to happen. In the spaces below, identify and write the missing part of each cause-and-effect relationship.

a. Cause: Sunlight penetrates layers of hyphae.

Effect: _____

b. Cause: _____

Effect: Lichens are able to survive harsh environments.

Suggestions for Use

Each worksheet is a student-centered activity that can be completed independently. The flexible structure of the worksheets permits a wide array of uses in the classroom. Possible methods of use include:

- **Prereading Activity** Before beginning a section, distribute the corresponding Active Reading Guide worksheet to the students. Have them preview the section by reading through the worksheet questions. Then read the textbook section aloud as a whole group activity, having students complete the worksheet as they come upon an answer. In this manner, previewing the section provides students with a motive for reading the section and helps direct their attention to certain key passages.

- **Postreading Activity** After reading a textbook section, distribute the corresponding Active Reading Guide worksheet to the students. Have them complete the worksheet independently and then check answers with a partner or in a small group. In this manner, the worksheet acts as a tool for assessing understanding of the section's key ideas.

ESL/LEP Students

The guide can also be used to address the unique language needs of ESL/LEP students. The following are specific suggestions for helping these students.

- Assessment scores often point out deficient skill areas of the test-taker. If assessment records are available, scan the reading/language results of low-scoring readers and note each student's problem areas.

Correlate the test results with the reading skill labels found on each worksheet. Select corresponding worksheets to create a mini-workbook for each student that targets his or her individual weaknesses.

- In many districts, support staff such as ESL teachers, basic skill teachers, and/or resource room teachers meet with low-scoring readers. Provide these instructors with Active Reading Guide worksheets that correlate with a week's worth of classroom instruction. Support staff can use the worksheets as the focus of parallel small-group instruction.

- Target a specific reading skill that needs to be reinforced. Select all of the Active Reading Guide worksheets that address this skill, and have students work through the worksheets in consecutive order. Since this method is not restricted to the location of content instruction, it focuses on a directed reading skill rather than biology content.

Extension Activities

The following activities can be used to extend the reading skills developed in the guide.

- Direct students to a passage that uses a particular text structure such as sequencing information. Challenge students to identify clue words that indicate this structure. Then have them complete a graphic organizer to show the steps of the process.

- Ask students to use a specific text structure to format their responses to an essay question.

- Have students create a graphic organizer that highlights the main idea and supporting details of a passage. You may wish to use one of the Reading Organizer worksheets found in the Holt BioSources Teaching Resources, located in the *Biology: Principles and Explorations* One-Stop Planner CD-ROM.

- Provide students with paper strips. Have them use the strips to create a physical model of a cause-and-effect text structure used in a passage. Have students label the first strip with the initial event described, or a cause. Have students label the next strip with the event that resulted, or an effect. This second event then acts as the cause of another event. When all strips have been labeled, have students attach the papers like links in a chain.

- Divide the class into small groups and provide each group with 16 index cards. Have the students work cooperatively to find eight cause and effect relationships in a chapter. Have students label each of eight index cards with a cause and the remaining cards with an effect. Have groups swap cards, shuffle the cards, and place them face down on a table. Have one member turn over two cards. If the cards display a cause and subsequent effect, the student keeps the cards. If the cards do not match, they are returned to their original position. Group members take turns displaying cards. When all cards have been picked up, the student with the greatest number of cards is the winner.

- Identify a key prefix such as *hydro-*. Have students scan the text to make a list of terms containing this prefix. Then have students define each entry on their list.

CHAPTER 1 **ACTIVE READING**

—Biology and You

► Section 1-1: Themes of Biology

Read the passage below, which is reproduced from page 8 of your textbook. Notice that the sentences are numbered. Answer the questions that follow.

[1] All living things are able to pass on their characteristics (traits) to their offspring because the genes that determine their characteristics are passed on from parent to offspring each generation. [2] **Genes** are sets of inherited instructions for making proteins that are coded in a molecule called deoxyribonucleic acid (DNA). [3] The passing of traits from parents to offspring is called **heredity.** [4] Heredity is the reason children tend to resemble their parents. [5] Sometimes damage causes genes to change. [6] A change in the DNA of a gene is called a **mutation.** [7] Mutations in sex cells (eggs and sperm) are passed on to other generations. [8] Mutations in body cells are not, but they may disrupt the control of cell reproduction, producing cancer.

Read each question and write your answer in the space provided.

SKILL: Reading Effectively

1. Why does the word *traits* appear in parentheses in Sentence 1?

_____

_____

_____

2. The word *genes* appears in boldface type in Sentence 2. What does the use of boldface type indicate?

_____

_____

_____

3. Based on Sentence 3, how would you define the word *heredity*?

_____

_____

_____

4. A cause-and-effect relationship is identified in Sentence 4. What is the effect of *heredity?*

_____

_____

5. Another cause-and-effect relationship is identified in Sentence 5. What causes *genes* to change?

_____

_____

6. What relationship is indicated by the parentheses in Sentence 7?

_____

_____

7. Sentence 8 describes two cause-and-effect relationships. What are they?

_____

_____

_____

_____

Circle the letter of the word or phrase that best completes the statement.

8. A change in the DNA of a gene is called a
   a. cancer.
   b. trait.
   c. mutation.
   d. sex cell.

CHAPTER 1 **ACTIVE READING**

Biology and You

▶ Section 1-2: Biology in Your World

Read the passage below, which is reproduced from page 10 of your textbook. Answer the questions that follow.

In 1999, the world's human population passed 6 billion people. As the population continues to grow, the demand for food is going to strain our ability to feed them. Biologists are vigorously seeking new crops that grow more efficiently in tropical soils and crops that grow without intensive use of fertilizers and insecticides. Genetic engineers are transplanting beneficial plant genes into other plants to create crops that are more resistant to insects and microorganisms. It is hoped that genetically engineered crops will both reduce the need for insecticides and increase crop yields. Some genetically-engineered plants are now resistant to frost damage because of new genes inserted into the plants. Other genetically-engineered crops are resistant to insects, allowing farmers to decrease or avoid the use of chemical pesticides.

Read each question and write your answer in the space provided.

SKILL: Recognizing Cause and Effect

1. The passage above identifies cause-and-effect relationships for the growing human population. Listed in the first column below are types of resistance in plants caused by genetic engineering. In the second column, list the beneficial effect the genetic engineering will produce for farmers.

Cause	Effect
Genetically engineered crops that are resistant to insects.	a.
Genetically engineered crops that are resistant to frost damage.	b.

(continued on next page)

2. What types of scientists are transplanting beneficial plant genes into other plants?

_____

3. How are plants genetically engineered?

_____

_____

4. What will be increasingly in demand as the human population continues to increase?

_____

Circle the letter of the word or phrase that best completes the statement.

5. Biologists are vigorously seeking new crops that will grow more efficiently in
   a. genetically engineered soils.
   b. tropical soils.
   c. microorganic soils.
   d. balanced soils.

Name _____ Date _____ Class _____

Biology and You

▶ Section 1-3: The Scientific Process

Read the passage below, which is reproduced from page 19 of your textbook. Answer the questions that follow.

Scientists make progress the same way a sculptor makes a marble statue—by chipping away at unwanted bits. If a hypothesis does not provide a reasonable explanation for what has been observed, the hypothesis is rejected. Scientists routinely make predictions and attempt to confirm them by testing one or more alternative hypotheses. A **theory** is a set of related hypotheses that have been tested and confirmed many times by many scientists. A theory unites and explains a broad range of observations.

Read each question and write your answer in the space provided.

SKILL: Reading Effectively

1. What causes a hypothesis to be rejected?

_____

_____

_____

_____

2. How do scientists confirm a prediction?

_____

_____

_____

3. How are a *theory* and a set of hypotheses related?

_____

_____

_____

_____

In the spaces provided, write the term or phrase from the Word Box that best completes each statement.

SKILL: Organizing Information

4. The graphic organizer below illustrates the making of a theory.

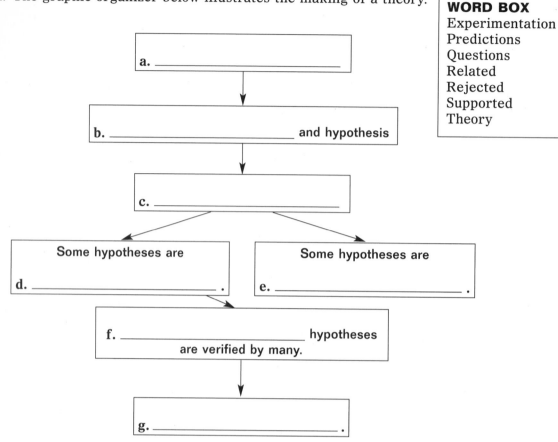

WORD BOX
Experimentation
Predictions
Questions
Related
Rejected
Supported
Theory

a. _____

b. _____ and hypothesis

c. _____

Some hypotheses are
d. _____ .

Some hypotheses are
e. _____ .

f. _____ hypotheses
are verified by many.

g. _____ .

Circle the letter of the word or phrase that best answers the question.

5. What is the first step in the formation of a theory?

   a. hypotheses

   b. communication

   c. experimentation

   d. observation

Chemistry of Life

▶ Section 2-1: Nature of Matter

Read the passage below, which is reproduced from page 29 of your textbook. Notice that the sentences are numbered. Answer the questions that follow.

[1] Covalent bonds are chemical bonds that form when two or more atoms share electrons to form a **molecule.** [2] A molecule is a group of atoms held together by covalent bonds. [3] Like the rivets and welds that connect steel girders in a skyscraper, covalent bonds join the atoms in molecules of living things. [4] Because the number of protons is equal to the number of electrons in a molecule, the molecule has no net electrical charge. [5] Some examples of molecules include carbon dioxide (CO_2), water (H_2O) and oxygen (O_2).

Read each question and write your answer in the space provided.

SKILL: Reading Effectively

1. What Key Term is defined in Sentence 1?

   _____

2. How are covalent bonds and atoms related?

   _____

   _____

3. Why does *molecule* appear in boldface type in Sentence 1?

   _____

   _____

4. An analogy is a comparison. What analogy is made in Sentence 3?

   _____

   _____

Circle the letter of the word or phrase that best completes the statement.

5. All of the following are examples of molecules EXCEPT
   a. carbon dioxide.
   b. hydrogen.
   c. water.
   d. oxygen gas.

Chemistry of Life

▶ Section 2-2: Water and Solutions

Read the passage below, which is reproduced from page 33 of your textbook. Notice that the sentences are numbered. Answer the questions that follow.

[1] Compounds that form when dissolved in water are called **acids.** [2] When an acid is added to water, the concentration of hydrogen ions in the solution is increased above that of pure water. [3] In contrast, compounds that reduce the concentration of hydrogen ions in a solution are called **bases.** [4] Many bases form hydroxide ions when dissolved in water.

[5] The pH scale measures the concentration of hydrogen ions in solutions. [6] Most solutions have a pH value between 0 and 14. [7] Pure water has a pH value of 7. [8] Acidic solutions have pH values below 7, and basic solutions have pH values above 7. [9] Stomach acid has a pH value of about 2 (very acidic). [10] Blood has a pH value of about 7.5 (slightly basic). [11] Household ammonia, which is very basic, has a pH value of about 12.

Read each question and write your answer in the space provided.

SKILL: Recognizing Cause and Effect

1. What Key Terms are contained in this passage? How do you know the word(s) are Key Terms?

_____

_____

2. Define each Key Term.

_____

_____

_____

_____

3. A cause-and-effect relationship is identified in Sentence 2. What is the effect of adding an *acid* to water?

_____

_____

SKILL: Recognizing Similarities and Differences

4. A Venn diagram is a type of graphic organizer used to identify similarities and differences between two concepts. Read each question and write your answer in the appropriate place on the diagram.

   a. In the left oval, list the key traits of acids.
   b. In the right oval, list the key traits of bases.
   c. In the area formed by the overlapping ovals, list traits shared by both acids and bases.

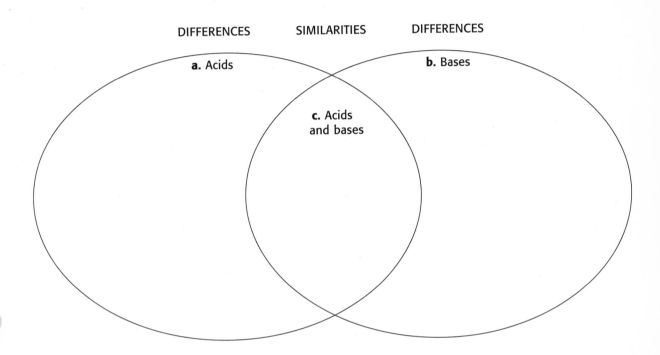

DIFFERENCES　　SIMILARITIES　　DIFFERENCES

a. Acids　　　　　　　　　　　　**b.** Bases

c. Acids and bases

Circle the letter of the number that best answers the question.

5. Which of the following pH values indicate a slightly acidic solution?

   a. 3
   b. 6.5
   c. 9
   d. 11

Chemistry of Life

▶ Section 2-3: Chemistry of Cells

Read the passage below, which is reproduced from page 34 of your textbook. Notice that the sentences are numbered. Answer the questions that follow.

[1] **Carbohydrates** are organic compounds made of carbon, hydrogen, and oxygen atoms in the proportion of 1:2:1. [2] Carbohydrates are a key source of energy, and they are found in most foods—especially fruits, vegetables, and grains. [3] The building blocks of carbohydrates are single sugars called **monosaccharides,** such as glucose, $C_6H_{12}O_6$, and fructose. [4] Glucose is a major source of energy in cells. [5] Disaccharides are double sugars formed when two monosaccharides are joined. [6] For example, sucrose, or common table sugar, consists of glucose and fructose. [7] Polysaccharides are chains of three or more monosaccharides. [8] A polysaccharide is an example of a macromolecule, a large molecule made up of many smaller molecules.

Read each question and write your answer in the space provided.

SKILL: Reading Effectively

1. What elements form an organic compound classified as a *carbohydrate*?

_____

_____

2. What does the 2 represent in the proportion given in Sentence 1?

_____

_____

3. What three food groups are good sources of *carbohydrates*?

_____

_____

4. The prefix *mono-* means "one." What word in Sentence 3 contains this prefix? What is the meaning of this word?

_____

_____

5. What chemical formula is given in Sentence 3? How many atoms are in a molecule of this compound?

_____

_____

6. The prefix *di-* means "two." What term in Sentence 5 contains this prefix? What is the meaning of this term?

_____

_____

7. In Sentence 6, which two *monosaccharides* join to form table sugar?

_____

_____

8. The prefix *poly-* means "more than one." What term in Sentence 7 contains this prefix? What is the meaning of this term?

_____

_____

Circle the letter of the word or phrase that best completes the statement.

9. An example of a macromolecule is a(n)

    a. oxygen atom.
    b. monosaccharide.
    c. glucose molecule.
    d. polysaccharide.

2 ACTIVE READING

Chemistry of Life

▶ Section 2-4: Energy and Chemical Reactions

Read the passage below, which is reproduced from page 41 of your textbook. Answer the questions that follow.

During a chemical reaction, a substance on which an enzyme acts is called a **substrate.** Enzymes act only on specific substrates. For example, the enzyme amylase assists in the breakdown of starch to glucose. In this reaction, starch is amylase's substrate.

An enzyme's shape determines its activity. Typically, an enzyme is a large protein with one or more deep folds on its surface. These folds form pockets called **active sites.** An enzyme's substrate fits into an active site.

Step 1: When an enzyme first attaches to a substrate during a chemical reaction, the enzyme's shape changes slightly so that the substrate fits more tightly in the enzyme's active site.

Step 2: At an active site, an enzyme and a substrate interact in a way that reduces the activation energy of the reaction, making the substrate more likely to react.

Step 3: The reaction is complete when products have formed. The enzyme is now free to catalyze further reactions.

Read each question and write your answer in the space provided.

SKILL: Reading Effectively

1. Define the two Key Terms contained in this passage.

_____

_____

_____

2. What substance is a *substrate* of amylase?

_____

_____

3. What determines an enzyme's activity?

_____

_____

SKILL: Interpreting Graphics

4. The figure below shows how enzymes work. In the space provided, describe what is occurring at each letter.

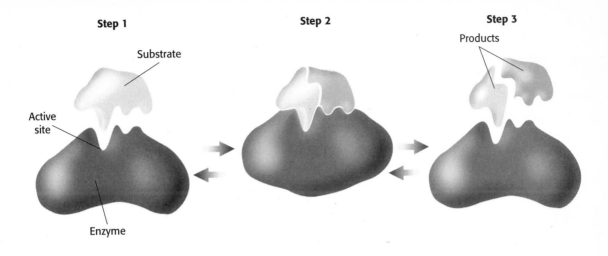

Step 1

Substrate

Active site

Enzyme

Step 2

Step 3

Products

a. **Step 1:** _____

_____

b. **Step 2:** _____

_____

c. **Step 3:** _____

_____

Circle the letter of the word or phrase that best answers the question.

5. What occurs when an enzyme and a substrate interact at an active site?
   a. activation energy is reduced
   b. the substrate changes shape
   c. the enzyme is changed by the reaction
   d. activation energy is increased

CHAPTER

3 **ACTIVE READING**

Cell Structure

▶ Section 3-1: Looking at Cells

Read the passage below, which is reproduced from page 50 of your textbook. Answer the questions that follow.

Measurements taken by scientists are expressed in metric units. The official name of the metric system is the International System of Measurements, abbreviated as SI. SI is a decimal system, so all relationships between SI units are based on powers of 10. For example, scientists measure the sizes of objects viewed under a microscope using the SI base unit for length, which is the meter. One meter (1 m), which is about 3.28 ft (a little more than a yard), equals 100 centimeters (cm), or 1,000 millimeters (mm). A meter also equals 0.001 kilometer (km). Most units have a prefix that indicates the relationship of that unit to the base unit. For example, the symbol μ stands for the metric prefix *micro*. A micrometer (μm) is a unit of linear measurement equal to one-millionth of a meter, or one-thousandth of a millimeter.

Read each question and write your answer in the space provided.

SKILL: Reading Effectively

1. How are the metric system and SI related?

_____

_____

2. Why are all relationships between SI units based on powers of 10?

_____

_____

3. What unit is used to measure the length of objects viewed under a microscope?

_____

_____

4. Why do most SI units contain a prefix?

_____

_____

5. Use information contained in the passage to complete the table.

Unit	Prefix	Metric equivalent
Kilometer (km)	a.	b.
Centimeter (cm)	c.	d.
Millimeter (mm)	e.	f.
Micrometer (μm)	g.	h.

Circle the letter of the word or phrase that best completes the statement.

6. A person who is 2 m tall is
   a. exactly 6 ft tall.
   b. less than 5 ft tall.
   c. a little more than 6 ft tall.
   d. a little more than 3 ft tall.

Name_____ Date _____ Class _____

Cell Structure

▶ Section 3-2: Cell Features

Read the passage below, which is reproduced from page 60 of your textbook. Answer the questions that follow.

Located in the lipid bilayer of the cell membrane are various proteins. The middle part of a membrane protein is mostly non-polar; it is attracted to the interior of the lipid bilayer but is repelled by the water on either side of the lipid bilayer. In contrast, the inner and outer parts of the protein are mostly polar and are therefore attracted to water. This dual attraction to water holds the protein in the lipid bilayer. However, the motion and fluidity of phospholipids enable the cell-membrane proteins to move around within the lipid bilayer.

There are different types of proteins in the cell membrane. Each type plays a vital role in the life of a cell. Marker proteins, which are attached to a carbohydrate on the cell's surface, help other cells recognize their cell type—liver cell or heart cell, for example. Receptor proteins recognize and bind to specific substances, such as signal molecules, outside the cell. Various enzymes in the cell membrane are involved in important biochemical reactions in the cell. Transport proteins aid the movement of substances into and out of the cell.

Read each question and write your answer in the space provided.

SKILL: Recognizing Cause and Effect

1. The first paragraph describes a cause-and-effect relationship between the structure of a membrane protein and the lipid bilayer. The cause in this relationship is the nonpolar middle part of a membrane protein. What is the effect?

_____

_____

_____

2. Another cause-and-effect relationship detailed in the first paragraph explains that the inner and outer parts of a membrane protein are mostly polar. What is the effect of this structure?

_____

_____

3. What causes a membrane protein to be held in the lipid bilayer?

_____

_____

4. The last sentence in the first paragraph describes another cause-and-effect relationship. Identify the cause and then the effect.

_____

_____

5. What is the main idea of the second paragraph?

_____

_____

SKILL: Organizing Information

6. The second paragraph of this passage identifies three different types of proteins found in the cell membrane and notes the function of each type. Complete the table below by writing the correct words or phrases in the spaces provided.

Type of protein	Function
a.	b.
c.	d.
e.	f.

Circle the letter of the word or phrase that best answers the question.

7. What is the function of enzymes found in the cell membrane?

    a. to move substances out of the cell
    b. to bind to specific substances
    c. to help cells recognize their cell type
    d. to aid biochemical reactions in the cell

CHAPTER
3 **ACTIVE READING**

Cell Structure

▶ Section 3-3: Cell Organelles

Read the passage below, which is reproduced from page 63 of your textbook. Notice that the sentences are numbered. Answer the questions that follow.

[1] Vesicles that contain newly made proteins move through the cytosol from the ER to an organelle called the **Golgi apparatus.** [2] The Golgi apparatus is a set of flattened, membrane-bound sacs that serves as the packaging and distribution center of the cell. [3] Enzymes inside the Golgi apparatus modify the proteins that are received in vesicles from the ER. [4] The modified proteins are then enclosed in new vesicles that bud from the surface of the Golgi apparatus. [5] Many of these vesicles move to the cell membrane and release their contents outside the cell. [6] Other vesicles include **lysosomes,** which are small, spherical organelles that contain the cell's digestive enzymes. [7] These vesicles stay within the cytoplasm. [8] Here, lysosomes digest and recycle the cell's used components by breaking down proteins, nucleic acids, lipids, and carbohydrates. [9] The ER, the Golgi apparatus, and lysosomes are involved in the production, packaging, and distribution of proteins.

Read each question and write your answer in the space provided.

SKILL: Reading Effectively

1. Describe the vesicles containing newly made proteins as stated in Sentence 1.

_____

_____

_____

2. What happens to the proteins once the vesicles reach the *Golgi apparatus*?

_____

_____

3. Where do the new vesicles come from?

_____

_____

4. What substances do *lysosomes* break down?

_____

_____

Circle the letter of the word or phrase that best completes the statement.

5. All of the following organelles are involved in the production, packaging, and distribution of proteins EXCEPT the
   a. Golgi apparatus.
   b. cytosol.
   c. ER.
   d. lysosomes.

CHAPTER

4 **ACTIVE READING**

Cells and Their Environment

▶ Section 4-1: Passive Transport

Read the passage below, which is reproduced from page 76 of your textbook. Notice that the sentences are numbered. Answer the questions that follow.

[1] The diffusion of water through a selectively permeable membrane is called **osmosis.** [2] Like other forms of diffusion, osmosis involves the movement of a substance—water—down its concentration gradient. [3] Osmosis is a type of passive transport.

[4] If the solutions on either side of the cell membrane have different concentrations of dissolved particles, they will also have different concentrations of "free" water molecules. [5]Osmosis will occur as water molecule diffuse into the solution with the lower concentration of free water molecules.

Read each question and write your answer in the space provided.

SKILL: Reading Effectively

1. What Key Term is defined in this passage? What does this term mean?

   _____

   _____

2. How are diffusion and *osmosis* related?

   _____

   _____

3. What does the word *water* in Sentence 2 tell you about *osmosis*?

   _____

   _____

Circle the letter of the word or phrase that best completes the statement.

4. Osmosis is a type of
   a. passive transport.
   b. diffusion.
   c. active transport.
   d. Both (a) and (b)

CHAPTER
4 **ACTIVE READING**

Cells and Their Environment

▶ Section 4-2: Active Transport

Read the passage below, which is reproduced from page 83 of your textbook. Answer the questions that follow.

The movement of a substance into a cell by a vesicle is called **endocytosis.** During endocytosis, the cell membrane forms a pouch around a substance outside the cell. The pouch then closes up and pinches off from the membrane to form a vesicle. Vesicles formed by endocytosis may fuse with lysosomes or other organelles. The movement of a substance by a vesicle to the outside of a cell is called **exocytosis.** During exocytosis, vesicles in the cell fuse with the cell membrane, releasing their contents. Cells use exocytosis to export proteins that are modified by the Golgi apparatus. Nerve cells and cells of various glands, for example, release proteins by exocytosis.

Read each question and write your answer in the space provided.

SKILL: Recognizing Similarities and Differences

1. Complete the table below. In the first column, write two characteristics of cells in endocytosis. In the second column, write two characteristics of cells in exocytosis.

Endocytosis	Exocytosis
a.	b.
c.	d.

(continued on next page)

2. The prefix *endo* -means "inside or within." How would knowing this prefix meaning help you define the Key Term *endocytosis*?

_____

_____

_____

_____

Circle the letter of the word or phrase that best completes the statement.

3. Through the process of exocytosis, nerve cells
   a. form vesicles.
   b. release proteins.
   c. fuse with lysosomes.
   d. Both (a) and (b)

CHAPTER

5 **ACTIVE READING**

Photosynthesis and Cellular Respiration

▶ Section 5-1: Energy and Living Things

Read the passage below, which is reproduced from page 94 of your textbook. Answer the questions that follow.

The process by which light energy is converted to chemical energy is called **photosynthesis.** Organisms that use energy from sunlight or inorganic substances to make organic compounds are called **autotrophs.** Most autotrophs, especially plants, are photosynthetic organisms. Some autotrophs, including certain bacteria, use inorganic substances to make organic compounds.

Organisms that must get energy from food instead of directly from sunlight or inorganic substances are called **heterotrophs.** Heterotrophs, including humans and other animals, get energy from food through the process of **cellular respiration.**

Read each question and write your answer in the space provided.

SKILL: Reading Effectively

1. The prefix *photo-* means "light." The root word *synthesis* comes from a Greek word that means "putting together." How could knowledge of these word parts help you define the word *photosynthesis?*

_____

_____

2. The prefix *auto-* means "self." The root word *troph* comes from a Greek word that means "to feed." How could knowledge of these word parts help you define the word *autotroph?*

_____

_____

3. The prefix *hetero-* comes from a Greek word that means "other." How could knowledge of this prefix and the root word *troph* help you define the word *heterotroph?*

_____

_____

4. An analogy is a comparison. Complete the analogy: Heterotrophs are to humans as

autotrophs are to _____. What relationship forms the
basis of this analogy?

_____

_____

5. How does cellular respiration help your body perform its life functions?

_____

_____

Circle the letter of the phrase that best answers the question.

6. Which of the following most closely resembles cellular respiration?
   a. warm water moving through copper pipes
   b. people moving along an escalator
   c. mixing different foods in a blender
   d. logs burning in a campfire

Name _____ Date _____ Class _____

Photosynthesis and Cellular Respiration

▶ Section 5-2: Photosynthesis

Read the passage below, which is reproduced from page 103 of your textbook. Answer the questions that follow.

Photosynthesis is directly affected by various environmental factors. The most obvious of these factors is light. In general, the rate of photosynthesis increases as light intensity increases until all of the pigments are being used. At this saturation point, the rate of photosynthesis levels off because pigments cannot absorb any more light. The carbon dioxide concentration affects the rate of photosynthesis in a similar manner. Once a certain concentration of carbon dioxide is present, photosynthesis cannot proceed any faster.

Photosynthesis is most efficient within a certain range of temperatures. Like all metabolic processes, photosynthesis involves many enzyme-assisted reactions. Enzymes operate properly only within certain temperature ranges.

Read each question and write your answer in the space provided.

SKILL: Reading Effectively

1. Write a sentence that identifies the main idea of this passage.

_____

_____

_____

2. What effect would a sudden decrease in light intensity have on the photosynthesis level of a particular plant?

_____

_____

_____

3. At what point does light intensity have little effect on the photosynthesis level of a plant?

_____

_____

_____

4. A study showed that the photosynthesis rate of a plant continually increased over a certain period. Then the rate leveled off. During the study, light intensity and temperature remained constant. The only variable was the concentration of carbon dioxide surrounding the plant. What was the cause of this variation in photosynthesis rate?

_____

_____

_____

5. In another study, the photosynthesis rate of a plant sharply decreased as air temperature sharply decreased. During this study, light intensity and concentration of carbon dioxide remained constant. What can you conclude about this variation?

_____

_____

_____

Circle the letter of the phrase that best answers the question.

6. Which of the following does not affect the photosynthesis rate of a plant?
   a. air temperature
   b. soil type
   c. light intensity
   d. carbon dioxide concentration

CHAPTER
5 **ACTIVE READING**

Photosynthesis and Cellular Respiration

▶ Section 5-3: Cellular Respiration

Read the passage below, which is reproduced from page 105 of your textbook. Answer the questions that follow.

In the first stage of cellular respiration, glucose is broken down in the cytoplasm during a process called **glycolysis.** Glycolysis is an enzyme-assisted anaerobic process that breaks down one six-carbon molecule of glucose to two three-carbon pyruvates. A molecule that has lost or gained one or more electrons is called an ion. Pyruvate is the ion of a three-carbon organic acid called pyruvic acid. The pyruvate molecules produced during glycolysis still contain some of the energy that was stored in the glucose molecule.

Read each question and write your answer in the space provided.

SKILL: Reading Effectively

1. What relationship exists between cytoplasm and glycolysis?

_____

2. *Glycolysis* is classified as an anaerobic process. What does this indicate?

_____

3. What happens to a six-carbon molecule of glucose during *glycolysis*?

_____

_____

4. What is the source of the energy contained in the pyruvate molecules produced through *glycolysis*?

_____

_____

Circle the letter of the word or phrase that best answers the question.

5. Which of the following is a product of glycolysis?
   a. two three-carbon molecules of pyruvate   **c.** cytosol
   b. two ATP molecules   **d.** both (a) and (b)

Chromosomes and Cell Reproduction

▶ Section 6-1: Chromosomes

Read the passage below, which is reproduced from page 119 of your textbook. Answer the questions that follow.

A **gene** is a segment of DNA that codes for a protein or RNA molecule. A single molecule of DNA has thousands of genes lined up like the cars of a train. When genes are being used, the strand of DNA is stretched out so that the information it contains can be decoded and used to direct the synthesis of proteins needed by the cell.

As a cell prepares to divide, the DNA and the proteins associated with the DNA coil into a structure called a **chromosome.** Before the DNA coils up, however, the DNA is copied. The two exact copies of DNA that make up each chromosome are called **chromatids.** The two chromatids, which become separated during cell division and are placed into each new cell, ensure that each new cell has the same genetic information as the original cell.

Read each question and write your answer in the space provided.

SKILL: Reading Effectively

1. How are *genes* and DNA related?

_____

_____

2. What occurs to a DNA strand as its genes are being used?

_____

_____

3. How are *chromatids* and *chromosomes* related?

_____

An analogy is a comparison. Circle the letter of the word or phrase that best completes the analogy.

4. A train is to cars as DNA is to
   a. chromatids.
   b. genes.
   c. proteins.
   d. RNA.

CHAPTER
6 **ACTIVE READING**

Chromosomes and Cell Reproduction

▶ ## Section 6-2: The Cell Cycle

Read the passage below, which is reproduced from page 125 of your textbook. Answer the questions that follow.

The **cell cycle** is a repeating sequence of cellular growth and division during the life of an organism. A cell spends 90 percent of its time in the first three phases of the cycle, which are collectively called **interphase.** A cell will enter the last two phases of the cell cycle only if it is about to divide.

The five phases of the cell cycle are as follows:

First growth (G1)phase: During the G_1 phase, a cell grows rapidly and carries out its routine functions. For most organisms, this phase occupies the major portion of the cell's life.

Synthesis (S) phase: A cell's DNA is copied during this phase. At the end of this phase, each individual chromosome consists of two chromatids attached at the centromere.

Second growth (G2) phase: In the G_2 phase, preparations are made for the nucleus to divide. Mitochondria and other organelles replicate. Hollow protein fibers called microtubules are assembled. The microtubules are used to move the chromosomes during mitosis.

Mitosis: The process during cell division in which the nucleus of a cell is divided into two nuclei is called **mitosis.** Each nucleus ends up with the same number and kinds of chromosomes.

Cytokinesis: The process during cell division in which the cytoplasm divides is called **cytokinesis.**

Read each question and write your answer in the space provided.

SKILL: Reading Effectively

1. What Key Terms are contained in this passage?

_____

_____

2. Give the meaning of these terms.

_____

_____

3. A cell viewed under a high-powered microscope appears to be in the fourth phase of the *cell cycle*. What does this indicate about the cell?

_____

_____

SKILL: Sequencing Information

4. Match each statement with the phase of the cell cycle it describes. Write the number corresponding to the correct phase in the spaces provided.

       1. first growth phase
       2. synthesis phase
       3. second growth phase
       4. mitosis
       5. cytokinesis

a. _____ nucleus divides

b. _____ makes up a major portion of most cells' lives

c. _____ cytoplasm divides

d. _____ mitochondria replicate

e. _____ cell grows rapidly

f. _____ two identical nuclei are produced

g. _____ DNA is copied

h. _____ microtubules are assembled

i. _____ forms two chromatids attached at the centromere

j. _____ cell carries out its routine functions

k. _____ microtubules move chromosomes

5. How are *mitosis* and *cytokinesis* alike? How do they differ?

_____

_____

_____

An analogy is a comparison. Circle the letter of the word or phrase that best completes the analogy.

6. G_2 phase is to mitochondria as S phase is to
  a. chromatids.
  b. centromere.
  c. microtubules.
  d. DNA.

CHAPTER 6 **ACTIVE READING**

Chromosomes and Cell Reproduction

▶ Section 6-3: Mitosis and Cytokinesis

Read the passage below, which is reproduced from page 131 of your textbook. Answer the questions that follow.

During cytokinesis, the cytoplasm of the cell is divided in half, and the cell membrane grows to enclose each cell, forming two separate cells as a result.

During cytokinesis in animal cells and other cells that lack cell walls, the cell is pinched in half by a belt of protein threads.

Plant cells and other cells that have rigid cell walls have different method of dividing the cytoplasm. In plant cells, vesicles formed by the Golgi apparatus fuse at the midline of the dividing cell and form a cell plate. A cell plate is a membrane-bound cell wall that forms across the middle of the cell. A new cell wall then forms on both sides of the cell plate.

Read each question and write your answer in the space provided.

SKILL: Reading Effectively

1. In the spaces provided, match each statement with the stage of cellular division it describes. For each of the statements below, write A if the statement is describing cytokinesis in animal cells, write P if it describes cytokinesis in plant cells, write B if it describes cytokinesis in both.

   a. _____ Golgi apparatus forms vesicles

   b. _____ two genetically identical cells are formed

   c. _____ belt of protein thread pinches cell in half

   d. _____ cell plate forms across the cell's middle

   e. _____ cytoplasm of the cell divides in half

   f. _____ cell wall forms on both sides of cell plate

An analogy is a comparison. Circle the letter of the word or phrase that best completes the analogy.

2. Plant cell is to cell plate as animal cell is to
   a. nucleus.
   b. cytoplasm.
   c. protein threads.
   d. Both (a) and (b)

Meiosis and Sexual Reproduction

Section 7-1: Meiosis

Read the passage below, which is reproduced from page 142 of your textbook. Answer the questions that follow.

Meiosis is a form of cell division that halves the number of chromosomes when forming specialized reproductive cells, such as gametes or spores. Meiosis involves two divisions of the nucleus—meiosis I and meiosis II—and each division is subdivided into stages.

The stages of meiosis I are as follows:

Prophase I: The chromosomes condense, and the nuclear envelope breaks down. Homologous chromosomes pair along their length and then cross over.

Metaphase I: The pairs of homologous chromosomes are moved by the spindle to the equator of the cell. The homologous chromosomes, each made up of two chromatids, remain together.

Anaphase I: The homologous chromosomes separate. As in mitosis, the chromosomes of each pair are pulled to opposite poles of the cell by the spindle fibers. But in meiosis, the chromatids do not separate at their centromeres.

Telophase I: Individual chromosomes gather at each of the poles. In most organisms, the cytoplasm divides, forming two new cells.

Read each question and write your answer in the space provided.

SKILL: Reading Effectively

1. Match each statement with the stage of meiosis I it describes by writing in the spaces provided, **PI** to represent Prophase I, **MI** to represent Metaphase I, **AI** to represent Anaphase I, or **TI** to represent Telophase I.

   a. _____ cytoplasm divides

   b. _____ nuclear envelope breaks down

   c. _____ homologous chromosomes separate

   d. _____ spindle moves homologous chromosomes to the cell's equator

   e. _____ crossing-over occurs

f. _____ two new cells form

g. _____ homologous chromosomes move to opposite poles of the cell

h. _____ chromosomes condense

Read the passage below, which is reproduced from page 143 of your textbook. Answer the questions that follow.

The stages of meiosis II are as follows:

Prophase II: A new spindle forms around the chromosomes.

Metaphase II: The chromosomes line up along the equator, attached at their centromeres to spindle fibers.

Anaphase II: The centromeres divide, and the chromatids (now called chromosomes) move to opposite poles of the cell.

Telophase II: A nuclear envelope forms around each set of chromosomes. The spindle breaks down, and the cell undergoes cytokinesis. The result of the two divisions of meiosis is four haploid cells.

2. Match each statement with the stage of meiosis II it describes by writing in the spaces provided, **PII** to represent Prophase II, **MII** to represent Metaphase II, **AII** to represent Anaphase II, or **TII** to represent Telophase II.

   a. _____ centromeres divide

   b. _____ new spindle forms

   c. _____ cell undergoes cytokinesis

   d. _____ chromosomes line up at equator

   e. _____ spindle breaks down

   f. _____ chromosomes move to opposite poles of the cell

   g. _____ four haploid cells form

Circle the letter of the word or phrase that best completes the statement.

3. Between meiosis I and meiosis II, chromosomes do not
   a. replicate.
   b. change position.
   c. divide.
   d. Both (a) and (b)

Name_____ Date _____ Class_____

Meiosis and Sexual Reproduction

▶ Section 7-2: Sexual Reproduction

Read the passage below, which is reproduced from page 148 of your textbook. Answer the questions that follow.

Reproduction, the process of producing offspring, can be asexual or sexual. In **asexual reproduction** a single parent passes copies of all of its genes to each of its offspring; there is no fusion of haploid cells such as gametes. An individual produced by asexual reproduction is a **clone,** an organism that is genetically identical to its parent. Prokaryotes reproduce by a type of asexual reproduction called binary fission. Many eukaryotes also reproduce asexually.

In contrast, in **sexual reproduction** two parents each form haploid reproductive cells, which join to form offspring. Since both parents contribute genetic material, the offspring have traits of both parents, but are not exactly like either parent. Sexual reproduction, with the formation of haploid cells, occurs in eukaryotic organisms.

Read each question and write your answer in the space provided.

SKILL: Reading Effectively

1. Write a sentence that states the main idea of this passage.

_____

_____

2. What is a *clone*?

_____

_____

3. What is one form of *asexual reproduction*?

_____

_____

4. Why do offspring produced through *sexual reproduction* show traits of each parent?

_____

_____

5. How are *sexual* and *asexual* reproduction alike?

_____

_____

6. How are *sexual* and *asexual* reproduction different?

_____

_____

An analogy is a comparison. Circle the letter of the word that best completes the analogy.

7. Asexual reproduction is to one as sexual reproduction is to
   a. many.
   b. fission.
   c. two.
   d. four.

CHAPTER
8 **ACTIVE READING**

Mendel and Heredity

▶ Section 8-1: The Origins of Genetics

Read the passage below, which is reproduced from page 162 of your textbook. Answer the questions that follow.

Mendel's initial experiments were monohybrid crosses. A **monohybrid cross** is a cross that involves one pair of contrasting traits. For example, crossing a plant with purple flowers and a plant with white flowers is a monohybrid cross. Mendel carried out his experiments in three steps.

Step 1: Mendel allowed each variety of garden pea plants to self-pollinate for several generations. This method ensured that each variety was **true-breeding** for a particular trait; that is, all the offspring would display only one form of a particular trait. For example, a true-breeding purple-flowering plant should produce only plants with purple flowers in subsequent generations.

These true-breeding plants served as the parental generation in Mendel's experiments. The parental generation, or **P generation,** are the first two individuals that are crossed in a breeding experiment.

Step 2: Mendel then cross-pollinated two P generation plants that had contrasting forms of a trait such as purple and white flowers. Mendel called the offspring of the P generation the first filial generation, or **F1 generation.** He then examined each F_1 plant and recorded the number of F_1 plants expressing each trait.

Step 3: Finally, Mendel allowed the F_1 generation to self-pollinate. He called the offspring of the F_1 generation plants the second filial generation, or **F2 generation.** Again, each F_2 plant was characterized and counted.

Read each question and write your answer in the space provided.

SKILL: Reading Effectively

1. The prefix *mono-* means "one." How does this apply to the Key Term *monohybrid cross?*

_____

_____

2. What information does the third sentence tell the reader?

_____

_____

3. Describe the offspring of a *true-breeding* white-flowering plant.

_____

_____

4. What is the *P generation?*

_____

_____

5. What does the term *F₁ generation* refer to?

_____

_____

SKILL: Interpreting Graphics

6. The figure below shows three generations of plants. Insert the following labels in the spaces provided: cross-pollination, F_1, F_2, P, self-pollination.

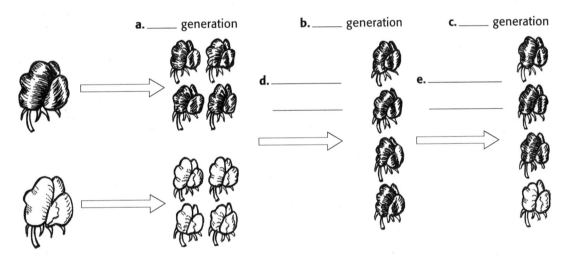

a. _____ generation   **b.** _____ generation   **c.** _____ generation

d. _____   **e.** _____

Circle the letter of the phrase that best completes the statement.

7. During the course of his experiment, Mendel studied traits in
   a. one generation of plants.
   b. two generations of plants.
   c. three generations of plants.
   d. more than five generations of plants.

Name_____ Date _____ Class _____

Mendel and Heredity

▶ Section 8-2: Mendel's Theory

Read the passage below, which is reproduced from page 165 of your textbook. Answer the questions that follow.

Geneticists have developed specific terms and ways of representing an individual's genetic makeup. Letters are often used to represent alleles. Dominant alleles are indicated by writing the first letter of the trait as a capital letter. Recessive alleles are also indicated by writing the first letter of the dominant trait, but the letter is lowercase.

If two alleles of a particular gene present in an individual are the same, the individual is said to be **homozygous** for that trait. If the alleles of a particular gene present in an individual are different, the individual is **heterozygous** for that trait.

Read each question and write your answer in the space provided.

SKILL: Reading Effectively

1. How are dominant alleles often represented?

_____

_____

2. How are recessive alleles often represented?

_____

_____

3. A particular plant is said to be *homozygous* for seed color. What does this mean?

_____

_____

4. Another plant is said to be *heterozygous* for flower color. What does this mean?

_____

_____

5. The allele for yellow peas is dominant to the allele for green peas. How would you represent the alleles of a plant that is *heterozygous* for seed color?

_____

_____

6. The allele for purple flowers is dominant to the allele for white flowers. How would you represent the alleles of a plant that is *homozygous* recessive for flower color?

_____

_____

7. How would you represent the alleles of a plant that is *heterozygous* for flower color?

_____

_____

Circle the letter of the phrase that best completes the statement.

8. A plant with YY alleles for seed color is
   a. heterozygous dominant for this trait.
   b. homozygous dominant for this trait.
   c. homozygous recessive for this trait.
   d. Either (a) or (b)

Mendel and Heredity

▶ Section 8-3: Studying Heredity

Read the passage below, which is reproduced from page 168 of your textbook. Answer the questions that follow.

A **Punnett square** is a diagram that predicts the expected outcome of a genetic cross by considering all possible combinations of gametes in the cross. Named for its inventor, Reginald Punnett, the Punnett square in its simplest form consists of four boxes inside a square. The possible gametes that one parent can produce are written along the top of the square. The possible gametes that the other parent can produce are written along the left side of the square. Each box inside the square is filled with two letters obtained by combining the allele along the top of the box with the allele along the side of the box. The letters in the boxes indicate the possible genotypes of the offspring.

Read each question and write your answer in the space provided.

SKILL: Reading Effectively

1. What information does the first sentence tell the reader?

   _____

   _____

2. What do letters written along the top and left side of a *Punnett square* represent?

   _____

   _____

3. How is the combination of letters inside each square determined?

   _____

   _____

4. What do the letters in the boxes indicate?

   _____

   _____

5. What data did Mendel obtain when he examined each F_1 plant?

_____

_____

SKILL: Organizing Information

6. The figure below shows a Punnett square. The Punnett square below shows a cross between two pea plants that are heterozygous for seed color. Use the Punnett square to answer the questions that follow. Write your answers in the spaces provided.

Yy
(Heterozygous)

Yy
(Heterozygous)

	Box 1	Yy
	Yy	Box 4

a. What pair of letters should appear in Box 1?

_____

b. What pair of letters should appear in Box 4?

_____

c. How many homozygous dominant offspring would be produced?

_____

d. How many homozygous recessive offspring would be produced?

_____

e. How many heterozygous offspring would be produced?

_____

f. How many of the offspring would have green seeds?

_____

g. How many of the offspring would have yellow seeds?

_____

Circle the letter of the word or phrase that best completes the statement.

7. Each box inside a Punnett square represents one
   a. allele.
   b. parent.
   c. dominant trait.
   d. offspring.

Mendel and Heredity

▶ Section 8-4: Patterns of Heredity Can Be Complex

Read the passage below, which is reproduced from page 176 of your textbook. Answer the questions that follow.

Genes with three or more alleles are said to have **multiple alleles.** When traits are controlled by genes with multiple alleles, an individual can have only two of the possible alleles for that gene. For example, in the human population, the ABO blood groups (blood types) are determined by three alleles, *IA, IB*, and *i*. The letters *A* and *B* refer to two carbohydrates on the surface of red blood cells. The *i* allele means that neither carbohydrate is present. The *IA* and *IB* alleles are both dominant over *i*, which is recessive. But neither *IA* nor *IB* is dominant over the other. When *IA* and *IB* are both present in the genotype, they are codominant.

Read each question and write your answer in the space provided.

SKILL: Reading Effectively

1. What information does the first sentence convey to the reader?

   _____

   _____

2. Why does the term *blood types* appear in parentheses in the third sentence of this passage?

   _____

   _____

3. What do the letters *A* and *B* refer to in the alleles I^A and I^B?

   _____

   _____

4. What allele is dominant for human blood type? What allele is recessive for this trait?

   _____

   _____

5. What causes an individual to show both the I^A and I^B forms of the trait for human blood type?

_____

_____

Circle the letter of the phrase that best completes the statement.

6. In humans, the *i* allele for blood type means that
   a. one kind of carbohydrate is on the surface of red blood cells.
   b. two kinds of carbohydrates are on the surface of red blood cells.
   c. more than three kinds of carbohydrates are on the surface of red blood cells.
   d. neither carbohydrate is present on the surface of red blood cells.

Name_____ Date _____ Class_____

—DNA: The Genetic Material

▶ Section 9-1: Identifying the Genetic Material

Read the passage below, which is reproduced from page 188 of your textbook. Answer the questions that follow.

In 1928, bacteriologist Frederick Griffith tried to prepare a vaccine against the pneumonia-causing bacterium *Streptococcus pneumoniae*. A **vaccine** is a substance that is prepared from killed or weakened microorganisms and is introduced into the body to protect the body against future infections by the microorganisms.

Griffith worked with two strains of *S. pneumoniae*. The first strain was enclosed in a capsule made of polysaccharides. The capsule protected the bacterium from the body's defense systems; this helped make the microorganism **virulent,** or able to cause disease. The second strain of *S. pneumoniae* lacked the polysaccharide capsule and did not cause disease.

Griffith knew that mice infected with *S* bacteria grew sick and died, while mice infected with *R* bacteria were not harmed. To determine if the capsule on the *S* bacteria was causing the mice to die, Griffith injected the mice with dead *S* bacteria. The mice remained healthy. Griffith then prepared a vaccine of weakened *S* bacteria by raising their temperature until the bacteria were "heat-killed," meaning they could no longer reproduce.

When Griffith injected the mice with the heat-killed *S* bacteria, the mice still lived. He then mixed the harmless live *R* bacteria with the harmless heat-killed *S* bacteria. Mice injected with this mixture died. When Griffith examined the blood of the dead mice, he found that the live *R* bacteria had acquired polysaccharide capsules. Somehow, the harmless *R* bacteria underwent a change and became live virulent *S* bacteria. This phenomenon is now called **transformation,** a change in phenotype caused when bacterial cells take up foreign genetic material.

Read each question and write your answer in the space provided.

SKILL: Reading Effectively

1. What effect does a *vaccine* have on the body?

_____

_____

2. What effect does a capsule made of polysaccharides have on a bacterium contained within the capsule?

_____

_____

3. What does the Key Term *virulent* mean?

_____

_____

4. What effect did an injection of dead *S* bacteria have on the mice Griffith studied?

_____

_____

5. What effect did an injection of heat-killed *S* bacteria have on the mice Griffith studied?

_____

_____

6. What effect did an injection of live *R* bacteria mixed with heat-killed *S* bacteria have on the mice?

_____

_____

7. What did Griffith discover when he examined the blood of the dead mice?

_____

_____

Circle the letter of the phrase that best completes the statement.

8. In order to determine whether the capsule on the *S* bacteria was causing mice to die, Griffith injected mice with
   a. dead *S* bacteria.
   b. weakened *S* bacteria.
   c. heat-killed *R* bacteria.
   d. Both (a) and (b)

Name _____ Date _____ Class _____

DNA: The Genetic Material

▶ Section 9-2: The Structure of DNA

Read the passage below, which is reproduced from page 192 of your textbook. Answer the questions that follow.

Watson and Crick determined that DNA is a molecule that is a **double helix**—two strands twisted around each other, like a winding staircase. Each strand is made of linked nucleotides. **Nucleotides** are the subunits that make up DNA. Each nucleotide is made of three parts: a phosphate group, a five-carbon sugar molecule, and a nitrogen base. The five-carbon sugar in DNA nucleotides is called **deoxyribose,** from which DNA gets its full name, deoxyribonucleic acid.

Read each question and write your answer in the space provided.

SKILL: Reading Effectively

1. What does the Key Term *double helix* mean?

_____

_____

2. What is the purpose of the phrase "like a winding staircase" in the first sentence?

_____

_____

3. Name another object that provides a visual model of a double helix.

_____

_____

4. In many words, the prefix *sub-* means "forming part of a whole." For example, a *sub*set is part of a set. Why then, are *nucleotides* called *sub*units of DNA?

_____

_____

5. What are the three subunits that make up a *nucleotide?*

_____

_____

6. What do the letters *DNA* stand for?

_____

_____

An analogy is a comparison. Circle the letter of the word or phrase that best completes the analogy.

7. DNA is to nucleotide as nucleotide is to
   a. deoxyribose.
   b. double helix.
   c. nucleic acid.
   d. Both (a) and (b)

Name_____ Date _____ Class _____

DNA: The Genetic Material

▶ Section 9-3: The Replication of DNA

Read the passage below, which is reproduced from page 196 of your textbook. Answer the questions that follow.

The process of making a copy of DNA is called **DNA replication.** It occurs during the synthesis (S) phase of the cell cycle, before a cell divides. The process can be broken down into three steps.

Step 1: Before replication can begin, the double helix must unwind. This is accomplished by enzymes called **DNA helicases,** which open up the double helix by breaking the hydrogen bonds that link the complimentary nitrogen bases. Once the two strands of DNA are separated, additional enzymes and other proteins attach to each strand, holding them apart and preventing them from twisting back into their double-helical shape. The two areas on either end of the DNA where the double helix separates are called **replication forks** because of their Y shape.

Step 2: At the replication fork, enzymes known as **DNA polymerases** move along each of the DNA strands, adding nucleotides to the exposed nitrogen bases according to the base-pairing rules. As the DNA polymerases move along, two new double helixes are formed.

Step 3: Once a DNA polymerase has begun adding nucleotides to a growing double helix, the enzyme remains attached until all of the DNA has been copied and it is signaled to detach. This process produces two DNA molecules, each composed of a new and an original strand. The nucleotide sequences in both of these DNA molecules are identical to each other and to the original DNA molecule.

Read each question and write your answer in the space provided.

SKILL: Reading Effectively

1. What is *replication?*

_____

_____

2. When does *replication* occur?

_____

_____

3. What must occur before *replication* can begin?

_____

_____

SKILL: Interpreting Graphics

4. The figure below shows DNA replicating. Describe what is occurring at each lettered section of the figure, in the space provided.

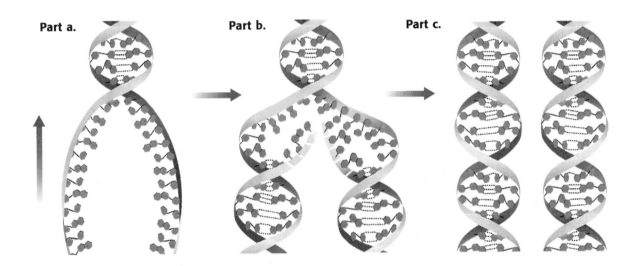

Part a. _____

_____

Part b. _____

_____

Part c. _____

_____

Circle the letter of the word or phrase that best completes the statement.

5. DNA helicases and DNA polymerases are alike in that both are types of
    a. nucleotides.   **c.** enzymes.
    b. nitrogen bases.   **d.** Both (a) and (b)

CHAPTER
10 **ACTIVE READING**

How Proteins Are Made

▶ Section 10-1: From Genes to Proteins

Read the passage below, which is reproduced from page 206 of your textbook. Answer the questions that follow.

Like DNA, **Ribonucleic acid (RNA)** is a nucleic acid—a molecule made of nucleotides linked together. RNA differs from DNA in three ways. First, RNA consists of a single strand of nucleotides instead of the two strands found in DNA. Second, RNA nucleotides contain the five-carbon sugar ribose rather than the sugar deoxyribose found in DNA nucleotides. And third, RNA has a nitrogen base called **uracil**—abbreviated as *U*—instead of the base thymine (T) found in DNA. Like thymine, uracil is complementary to adenine whenever RNA base-pairs with another nucleic acid.

Read each question and write your answer in the space provided.

SKILL: Recognizing Similarities and Differences

1. In the spaces provided, write *D* on the line if the statement is true of DNA. Write *R* on the line if the statement is true of RNA. Write *B* on the line if the statement is true of both DNA and RNA.

   a. _____ consists of a single strand of nucleotides

   b. _____ made of nucleotides linked together

   c. _____ contains deoxyribose

   d. _____ has the nitrogen base uracil

   e. _____ contains ribose

   f. _____ is a nucleic acid

   g. _____ consists of a double strand of nucleotides

   h. _____ contains a base that pairs with adenine

An analogy is a comparison. Circle the letter of the word or phrase that best completes the analogy.

2. RNA is to *U* as DNA is to
   a. *C*   **c.** *T*
   b. *G*   **d.** *A*

How Proteins Are Made

▶ **Section 10-2: Gene Regulation and Structure**

Read the passage below, which is reproduced from page 217 of your textbook. Answer the questions that follow.

A change in the DNA of a gene is called a mutation. The effects of a mutation vary, depending on whether it occurs in a gamete or in a body cell. Mutations in gametes can be passed on to offspring of the affected individual, but mutations in body cells affect only the individual in which they occur. Mutations that change one or just a few nucleotides in a gene on a chromosome are called **point mutations.** There are two general types of point mutations. In the first type, one nucleotide in a gene is replaced with a different nucleotide. Such a point mutation is called a substitution.

A point mutation can result in a protein not being made at all or a protein with a different amino acid so that the protein does not function. Sometimes substitutions have little or no effect.

In a second type of point mutation, one or more nucleotides are added to or deleted from a gene. These point mutations are known as insertions and deletions. Because the genetic message is read as a series of triplet nucleotides, insertions and deletions of one or two nucleotides can catastrophically upset the triplet groupings.

Read each question and write your answer in the space provided.

SKILL: Reading Effectively

1. What is a mutation?

_____

_____

2. A certain mutation is passed to offspring of the affected individual. What does this indicate about the type of cell in which the mutation originally occurred?

_____

_____

3. Describe the relationship between a substitution and a *point mutation*.

_____

_____

4. What is an insertion?

_____

_____

5. Why can a deletion have potentially catastrophic results?

_____

_____

Circle the letter of the phrase that best completes the statement.

6. A mutation in a body cell is similar to a mutation in a gamete in that both involve
   a. offspring of the affected individual.
   b. a change in the DNA of a gene.
   c. addition of nucleotides.
   d. deletion of nucleotides.

Gene Technology

▶ Section 11-1: Genetic Engineering

Read the passage below, which is reproduced from page 227 of your textbook. Answer the questions that follow.

Genetic engineering experiments use different approaches, but most share four basic steps.

Step 1: Cutting DNA. The DNA from the organism containing the gene of interest and the DNA from a vector are cut. The DNA is cut into pieces by restriction enzymes. **Restriction enzymes** are bacterial enzymes that recognize and bind to specific short sequences of DNA and then cut the DNA between specific nucleotides within the sequences. A **vector** is an agent that is used to carry the gene of interest into another cell. Commonly used vectors include viruses, yeast, and plasmids. **Plasmids** are circular DNA molecules that can replicate independently of the main chromosome of the bacteria. Plasmids are usually found in bacteria.

Step 2: Making Recombinant DNA. The DNA fragments from the organism containing the gene of interest are combined with the DNA fragments from the vector. An enzyme called DNA ligase is added to help bond the DNA fragments together.

Step 3: Cloning. Cells are treated so that they can take up the recombinant DNA. In a process called **gene cloning,** many copies of the gene of interest are made each time the host cell reproduces. Since bacteria reproduce by binary fission, when a bacterial cell replicates its DNA, it also replicates its plasmid DNA.

Step 4: Screening. Cells that have received the particular gene of interest are distinguished from the cells that did not take up the vector with the gene of interest. Each time the cells reproduce, they make a copy of the gene of interest. The cells can transcribe and translate the gene to make the protein coded for in the gene.

(continued on next page)

Read each question and write your answer in the space provided.

SKILL: Reading Effectively

1. What are *restriction enzymes*?

_____

_____

2. What is a *vector*?

_____

_____

3. How are *vectors* and *plasmids* related?

_____

_____

4. What is the function of DNA ligase in genetic engineering?

_____

_____

5. What is the product of *gene cloning?*

_____

_____

6. How does the reproductive method of bacteria ensure the replication of plasmid DNA?

_____

_____

_____

_____

Circle the letter of the word or phrase that best completes the statement.

7. All of the following are commonly used as vectors EXCEPT
   a. yeast.
   b. plasmids.
   c. DNA ligase.
   d. viruses.

Name_____ Date _____ Class _____

—Gene Technology

▶ **Section 11-2: Genetic Engineering in Medicine and Society**

Read the passage below, which is reproduced from page 232 of your textbook. Answer the questions that follow.

Many viral diseases, such as smallpox and polio, cannot be treated effectively by existing drugs. Instead they are combated by prevention, using vaccines. A **vaccine** is a solution containing a harmless version of a pathogen (disease-causing microorganism). When a vaccine is injected, the immune system recognizes the pathogen's surface proteins and responds by making defensive proteins called antibodies. In the future, if the same pathogen enters the body, the antibodies are there to combat the pathogen and stop its growth before it can cause disease.

Traditionally, vaccines have been prepared either by killing a specific pathogenic microbe or by making the microbe unable to grow. This ensures that the vaccine itself will not cause the disease. The problem with this approach is that there is a small but real danger that a failure in the process to kill or weaken the pathogen will result in transmission of the disease to the very patients seeking protection. This danger is one of the reasons why rabies vaccines are administered only when a person has actually been bitten by an animal suspected of carrying rabies.

Read each question and write your answer in the space provided.

SKILL: Reading Effectively

1. What two viral diseases are identified in the first sentence of the passage?

_____

_____

2. What is a *vaccine*?

_____

_____

3. Why are the words enclosed by parentheses in the third sentence?

_____

_____

4. One action of a body's immune system is to recognize a pathogen's surface proteins. What causes this action?

_____

_____

5. What is the effect of the immune system's action identified in question 4?

_____

_____

6. What two actions are taken to ensure that a vaccine will not cause disease?

_____

_____

_____

Circle the letter of the word or phrase that best completes the statement.

7. Rabies vaccines are administered only when a person has been bitten by an animal suspected of carrying rabies because it is possible that the

　a. person receiving the vaccine may be allergic to it.
　b. pathogen may not have been killed or sufficiently weakened.
　c. animal may have a viral disease.
　d. Both (a) and (b)

CHAPTER
11 ACTIVE READING

Gene Technology

▶ Section 11-3: Genetic Engineering in Agriculture

Read the passage below, which is reproduced from page 239 of your textbook. Answer the questions that follow.

In 1997, a scientist named Ian Wilmut captured worldwide attention when he announced the first successful cloning using differentiated cells from an adult animal. A differentiated cell is a cell that has specialized to become a specific type of cell (such as a liver or udder cell). A lamb was cloned from the nucleus of an udder (mammary) cell taken from an adult sheep. Previously, scientists thought that cloning was only possible using embryonic or fetal cells that have not yet differentiated. Scientists thought that differentiated cells could not give rise to an entire organism. Wilmut's experiment proved otherwise.

An electric shock was used to fuse mammary cells from one sheep with egg cells without nuclei from a different sheep. The fused cells divided to form embryos, which were implanted into surrogate mothers. Only one embryo survived. Dolly, born on July 5, 1996, was genetically identical to the sheep that provided the mammary cell.

Read each question and write your answer in the space provided.

SKILL: Reading Effectively

1. What announcement did Ian Wilmut make in 1997?

_____

_____

_____

2. What is a differentiated cell?

_____

_____

3. Why is the word *mammary* enclosed in parentheses in the third sentence?

_____

_____

4. What notions regarding cloning did Wilmut's experiment disprove?

_____

_____

_____

_____

SKILL: **Sequencing Information**

5. Sequence the steps of Wilmut's experiment by writing the correct number in the space provided. Write _1_ on the line of the first step, _2_ on the line of the second step, and so on.

a. _____ Fused cells divided to form embryos.

b. _____ Mammary cells and egg cells were taken from two sheep.

c. _____ Dolly was born.

d. _____ Embryos were implanted into surrogate mothers.

e. _____ Electric shock was used to fuse cells.

Circle the letter of the word or phrase that best completes the statement.

6. Dolly was genetically identical to the sheep that
  a. provided the mammary cell.
  b. was the surrogate mother.
  c. provided the egg cells.
  d. Both (a) and (b)

CHAPTER
12 **ACTIVE READING**

History of Life on Earth

▶ Section 12-1: How Did Life Begin?

Read the steps below which are reproduced from pages 255 of your textbook. Answer the questions that follow.

Listed below are the steps of Louis Lerman's bubble model.

Step 1: Eruption of undersea volcanoes produces ammonia, methane, and other gases that become trapped in underwater bubbles.

Step 2: Protected by bubbles, gases needed to make amino acids undergo chemical reactions.

Step 3: As bubbles burst on the water's surface, simple organic molecules are released into the air.

Step 4: The simple organic molecules are carried upward by the wind and exposed to ultraviolet radiation and lightning. The additional energy they produce causes further reactions.

Step 5: Complex organic molecules fall into the oceans.

Read each question and write your answer in the space provided.

SKILL: Organizing Information

1. What gases were produced by the eruption of undersea volcanoes?

_____

2. What were the simple organic molecules exposed to, as they were carried upward by wind?

_____

3. After undergoing further reactions caused by exposure to ultraviolet radiation and lighting, what did organic molecules form?

_____

Circle the letter of the phrase that best completes the statement.

4. According to Lerman's bubble model, the key processes that formed the chemicals needed for life took place
   a. at the same rate as the "primordial soup" model.
   b. more slowly than what is estimated by the "primordial soup" model.
   c. within bubbles on the ocean's surface.
   d. on land rather than on a watery surface.

History of Life on Earth

▶ Section 12-2: Complex Organisms Developed

Read the passage below, which is reproduced from page 258 of your textbook. Answer the questions that follow.

Early in the history of life, two different groups of prokaryotes evolved—eubacteria and archaebacteria. Living examples include *Escherichia coli*, a species of eubacteria and *Sulfolobus*, a group of archaebacteria. **Eubacteria** are prokaryotes that contain a chemical called peptidoglycan in their cell walls and have the same type of lipids in their cell membranes that eukaryotes do. Eubacteria include many bacteria that cause disease and decay. **Archaebacteria** are prokaryotes that lack peptidoglycan in their cell walls and have unique lipids in their cell membranes. Archaebacteria are thought to be closely related to the first bacteria to have existed on Earth. Chemical evidence indicates that the first eukaryotic cells are more likely to have evolved from archaebacteria than from eubacteria.

Read each question and write your answer in the space provided.

SKILL: Reading Effectively

1. How are *eubacteria* and *archaebacteria* alike?

   _____

2. What relationship exists between *Sulfolobus* and *archaebacteria*?

   _____

3. What two traits of *eubacteria* are identified in the third sentence of this passage?

   _____

   _____

4. What two traits of *archaebacteria* are identified in the fifth sentence of this passage?

   _____

   _____

5. What unique trait of *archaebacteria* is described in the sixth sentence?

_____

_____

6. What evidence supports this idea?

_____

_____

An analogy is a comparison. Circle the letter of the word or phrase that best completes the analogy.

7. Archaebacteria is to *Sulfolobus* as eubacteria is to
    a. *Escherichia coli.*
    b. cyanobacteria.
    c. peptidoglycan.
    d. Both (a) and (b)

History of Life on Earth

▶ Section 12-3: Life Invaded the Land

Read the passage below, which is reproduced from page 267 of your textbook. Answer the questions that follow.

The first vertebrates to inhabit the land were early amphibians. Amphibians are smooth-skinned organisms that include frogs, toads, and salamanders.

Amphibians were able to adapt to land because of the development of several structural changes in their bodies. Early amphibians had moist breathing sacs called lungs, which they used to absorb oxygen from air. The limbs of amphibians are thought to be derived from the bones of fish fins. What made walking possible was the evolution of a strong support system of bones in the region just behind the head. This system of bones provided a rigid base for the limbs to work against.

Read each question and write your answer in the space provided.

SKILL: Reading Effectively

1. What three types of amphibians are identified in the passage?

_____

_____

2. What made it possible for amphibians to adapt to life on land?

_____

_____

3. According to the passage, the limbs of an amphibian were derived from what structure?

_____

_____

Circle the letter of the phrase that best completes the statement.

4. Jawless fishes and salamanders are alike in that both types of animals
   a. are amphibians.
   b. have backbones.
   c. have fins.
   d. are smooth-skinned organisms.

CHAPTER
13 **ACTIVE READING**

The Theory of Evolution

▶ Section 13-1: The Theory of Evolution by Natural Selection

Read the passage below, which is reproduced from page 279 of your textbook. Answer the questions that follow.

Darwin realized that Malthus's ideas about the human population apply to all species. Every organism has the potential to produce many offspring during its lifetime. In most cases, however, only a limited number of those offspring survive to reproduce. Adding Malthus's view to what he saw on his voyage and to his own experiences in breeding domestic animals, Darwin made a key association: *Individuals with physical or behavioral traits that better suit their environment are more likely to survive and reproduce than those without such traits.* Darwin suggested that by surviving long enough to reproduce, individuals have the opportunity to pass on their favorable characteristics to offspring. In time these favorable characteristics will increase in a population, and the nature of the population will gradually change. Darwin called this process by which populations change in response to their environment **natural selection.**

Read each question and write your answer in the space provided.

SKILL: Reading Effectively

1. Based on the first three sentences of this passage, what can the reader infer was Malthus's idea about the human population?

_____

_____

_____

2. What real-life experiences of his own did Darwin reflect upon when considering Malthus's ideas about the human population?

_____

_____

_____

3. According to Darwin, what causes the nature of a population to change?

_____

_____

_____

_____

Read this second passage below, which is reproduced from page 281 of your textbook. Answer the questions that follow.

Scientists now know that genes are responsible for inherited traits. Therefore, certain forms of a trait become more common in a population because more individuals in the population carry the alleles for those forms. In other words, natural selection causes the *frequency* of certain alleles in a population to increase or decrease over time. Mutations and the recombination of alleles that occurs during sexual reproduction provide endless sources of new variations for natural selection to act upon.

Read each question and write your answer in the space provided.

SKILL: Reading Effectively

4. What controls inherited traits?

_____

_____

5. What causes a particular trait to become more common in a population?

_____

_____

6. What two events cause new variations of traits in a population?

_____

_____

An analogy is a comparison. Circle the letter of the word or phrase that best completes the analogy.

7. Traits are to genes as variations are to
   a. populations.
   b. asexual reproduction.
   c. the environment.
   d. mutations.

CHAPTER

13 **ACTIVE READING**

The Theory of Evolution

▶ Section 13-2: Evidence of Evolution

Read the passage below, which is reproduced from page 289 of your textbook. Answer the questions that follow.

For decades, most biologists have understood evolution as a gradual process that occurs all the time. The model of evolution in which gradual change over a long period of time leads to species formation is called **gradualism.** But American biologists Stephen Jay Gould and Niles Eldredge have suggested that successful species stay unchanged for long periods of time. Gould and Eldredge hypothesize that major environmental changes in the past have caused evolution to occur in spurts. This model of evolution, in which periods of rapid change in species are separated by periods of little or no change, is called **punctuated equilibrium.**

Read each question and write your answer in the space provided.

SKILL: Recognizing Similarities and Differences

1. Write *G* if the statement is true of gradualism, write *PE* if the statement is true of punctuated equilibrium, and *B* if the statement is true of both models.

   a. _____ change occurs in spurts

   b. _____ causes formation of new species

   c. _____ occurs at a steady rate

   d. _____ affected by environmental changes

   e. _____ occurs at an uneven rate

   f. _____ model of evolution

   g. _____ includes periods without change

   h. _____ goes on all the time

Circle the letter of the word or phrase that best answers the question.

2. According to Gould and Eldredge, which of the following events would cause a species to change rapidly?
   a. mutation   c. snowstorm
   b. volcanic eruption   d. both (a) and (b)

CHAPTER
(13) ACTIVE READING

—The Theory of Evolution

► Section 13-3: Examples of Evolution

The figure below is reproduced from page 292 of your textbook and shows beak-size variations in finches. Using the information contained in the figure, answer each question in the space provided.

Beak-Size Variation

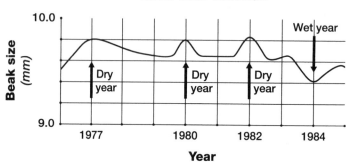

SKILL: Interpreting Graphics

1. The title of a graph indicates the type of information it contains. What is the title of the graph shown? Based on this title, what type of information can an observer expect to find?

_____

_____

_____

_____

2. Read the label on the horizontal axis of the graph. What information is plotted along this axis?

_____

_____

3. What intervals are used on the horizontal axis?

_____

_____

4. Read the label on the vertical axis of the graph. What information is plotted along this axis?

_____

5. What intervals are used on the vertical axis?

_____

_____

6. Based on the data shown, what effect does a dry year have on beak size?

_____

_____

7. Based on the data shown, what effect does a wet year have on beak size?

_____

_____

Circle the letter of the dates that best answers the question.

8. During which two years was the average finch beak size nearly the same?
   a. 1976 and 1982
   b. 1977 and 1979
   c. 1979 and 1981
   d. 1980 and 1983

Human Evolution

▶ Section 14-1: The Evolution of Primates

Read the passage below, which is reproduced from page 302 of your textbook. Answer the questions that follow.

The first primates evolved about 50 to 60 million years ago. These animals had two features that enabled them to stalk and capture insect prey in the branches of trees.

Unlike the clawed, unbendable toes of their ancestors, primates have grasping hands and feet that enable them to cling to their mothers when they are young, grip limbs, hang from branches, and seize food.

Unlike the eyes of their ancestors, which were located on the sides of the head, the eyes of primates are positioned at the front of the face. This forward placement of the eyes produces overlapping "binocular vision" that enables the primate brain to judge distance more precisely.

Read each question and write your answer in the space provided.

SKILL: Organizing Information

1. What information is provided by the first sentence of the passage?

   _____

   _____

2. Complete the table comparing the features of primates and their ancestors.

Primate ancestor features	Primate features
a.	b.
c.	d.

Circle the letter of the word or phrase that best completes the statement.

3. Binocular vision helps an organism's brain
   a. determine how far away a predator is.
   b. find a suitable habitat.
   c. recall information.
   d. solve a problem.

Human Evolution

▶ Section 14-2: Early Hominids

Read the passage below, which is reproduced from page 306 of your textbook. Answer the questions that follow.

Our earliest known direct ancestors belong to the group *Australopithecus*. Fossils indicate that australopithecines had two key hominid characteristics. First, they were fully **bipedal,** meaning they were able to walk upright on two legs. The structure of the ape skeleton makes walking upright for a long period of time difficult for apes. However, the structure of the australopithecine skeletons enabled them to be fully bipedal. The second hominid characteristic australopithecines exhibited was a large brain—which had a greater volume relative to body weight than the brain of an ape.

Read each question and write your answer in the space provided.

SKILL: Reading Effectively

1. What does fossil evidence suggest about our earliest known direct ancestors?

_____

_____

2. The prefix *bi-* means "two." How does this prefix apply to the Key Term *bipedal*?

_____

_____

3. What effect did the structure of an ape's skeleton have on the organism's ability to move from place to place?

_____

_____

4. What effect did the structure of the australopithecine skeleton have on the organism's ability to move from place to place?

_____

_____

5. How did the australopithecine brain compare with that of apes?

_____

_____

Circle the letter of the word or phrase that best completes the statement.

6. Bipedal is a trait of
   a. hominids.
   b. australopithecines.
   c. apes.
   d. Both (a) and (b)

Name_____ Date _____ Class _____

⟜—Human Evolution

▶ Section 14-3: The Genus *Homo*

Read the passage below, which is reproduced here from page 312 of your textbook. Answer the questions that follow.

Members of the genus *Homo* first appeared in Europe about 130,000 years ago. Fossils of the first *Homo* members, called Neanderthals, were found in 1856 in the Neander Valley of Germany. The Neanderthals were short and powerfully built. Their skulls were massive. They had protruding faces and heavy, bony ridges over the brows. Their brains were larger than those of modern humans.

Rare at first outside of Africa, Neanderthals became more and more abundant in Europe and Asia, and by 70,000 years ago, they had become fairly common. Neanderthals took care of their injured and sick, and they commonly buried their dead, often placing food, weapons, and even flowers with the bodies. Such attention to the dead suggests that they may have believed in a life after death. Neanderthals were the first hominids to show evidence of abstract thinking.

Read each question and write your answer in the space provided.

SKILL: Reading Effectively

1. When and where did *Homo sapiens* first appear?

_____

_____

2. Describe the difference between Neanderthals and modern humans.

_____

_____

3. Why do scientists believe that Neanderthals may have believed in a life after death?

_____

_____

Circle the letter of the word or phrase that best completes the statement.

4. Neanderthals were the first hominids to show evidence of
   a. language.   **c.** social organization.
   b. abstract thinking.   **d.** relocation.

Classification of Organisms

▶ Section 15-1: Categories of Biological Classification

Read the passage below, which is reproduced from page 322 of your textbook. Answer the questions that follow.

Linnaeus worked out a broad system of classification for plants and animals in which an organism's form and structure are the basis for arranging specimens in a collection. He later organized the genera and species that he described into a ranked system of groups that increase in inclusiveness. The different groups into which organisms are classified have expanded since Linnaeus's time and now consist of seven levels. Similar genera are grouped into a family.

Similar families are combined into an order. Orders with common properties are united in a class. Classes with similar characteristics are assigned to a phylum. Similar phyla are collected into a kingdom. There are six kingdoms of living things—the two kingdoms of bacteria, Archaebacteria and Eubacteria are prokaryotes. The other four kingdoms are Protista, Fungi, Plantae, and Animalia. The seven-level system can be divided into more specific categories, such as superclass, subclass, superorder, and suborder. In all, more than 30 taxonomic levels are recognized.

Read each question and write your answer in the space provided.

SKILL: Reading Effectively

1. What did Linnaeus use as the basis for classifying organisms in a collection?

_____

_____

2. The second sentence of this passage states that Linnaeus described a "ranked system of groups that increase in inclusiveness." What does this mean?

_____

_____

_____

3. How many kingdoms exist in the modern system of classification? What are they?

_____

_____

SKILL: Interpreting Graphics

4. The figure below shows the seven levels of the classification system. Using the information contained in the passage, insert the correct label in the space provided on the left side of the figure. On the right side of the figure, compose a sentence that describes the level. The first one has been done for you.

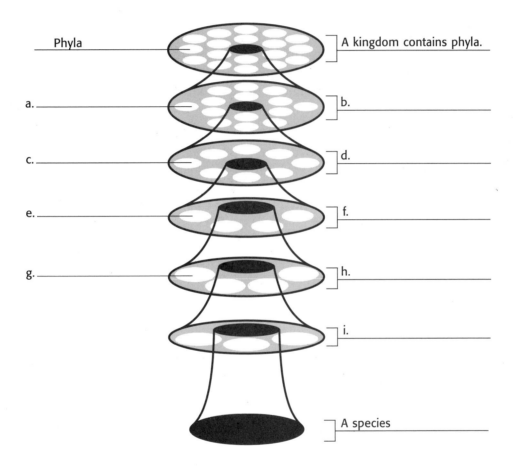

Phyla — A kingdom contains phyla.

a. _____

b. _____

c. _____

d. _____

e. _____

f. _____

g. _____

h. _____

i. _____

A species _____

An analogy is a comparison. Circle the letter of the word or phrase that best completes the analogy.

5. Class is to order as order is to
   a. kingdom.
   b. species.
   c. phylum.
   d. families.

Name_____ Date _____ Class _____

Classification of Organisms

► Section 15-2: How Biologists Classify Organisms

Read the passage below, which is reproduced from page 327 of your textbook. Answer the questions that follow.

Cladistics is a system of taxonomy that reconstructs phylogenies by inferring relationships based on similarities derived from a common ancestor. Cladistics is used to determine the sequence in which different groups of organisms evolved. To do this, cladistics focuses on a set of unique characteristics found in a particular group of organisms. These unique characteristics are called **derived traits.** Using patterns of shared derived traits, a biologist using cladistics constructs a branching diagram called a **cladogram,** which shows the evolutionary relationships among groups of organisms. The key to cladistics is identifying morphological, physiological, molecular, or behavioral traits that differ among the organisms being studied and that can be attributed to a common ancestor.

Read each question and write your answer in the space provided.

SKILL: Reading Effectively

1. How does *cladistics* reconstruct phylogenies?

_____

_____

2. What type of information is determined through *cladistics*?

_____

_____

3. How are *derived traits* and *cladistics* related?

_____

_____

_____

_____

4. What type of information does a *cladogram* show?

_____

_____

5. What type of traits do biologists focus on when creating a *cladogram*?

_____

_____

_____

_____

Circle the letter of the word or phrase that best completes the statement.

6. Derived traits are a set of unique characteristics
   a. found in a single species.
   b. which mammals lack.
   c. found in a particular group of organisms.
   d. Both (a) and (b)

Populations

▶ Section 16-1: How Populations Grow

Read the passage below, which is reproduced from page 341 of your textbook. Answer the questions that follow.

Every population has features that help determine its future. One of the most important features of any population is its size. The number of individuals in a population, or **population size,** can affect the population's ability to survive. Studies have shown that very small populations are among those most likely to become extinct.

A second important feature of a population is its density. **Population density** is the number of individuals that live in a given area. If the individuals of a population are few and spaced widely apart, they may seldom encounter one another, making reproduction rare.

A third feature of a population is the way the individuals of the population are arranged in space. This feature is called **dispersion.** Three main patterns of dispersion are possible within a population. If the individuals are randomly spaced, the location of each individual is self-determined. If individuals are evenly spaced, they are located at regular intervals. In a clumped distribution, individuals are bunched together in clusters. Each of these patterns reflects the interactions between the population and its environment.

Read each question and write your answer in the space provided.

SKILL: Reading Effectively

1. What are three key features of a population?

_____

_____

2. What do studies indicate about very small populations?

_____

_____

3. What is *population density*?

_____

_____

4. Describe a situation in which *population density* has a negative impact on the production of offspring.

_____

_____

_____

_____

SKILL: **Interpreting Graphics**

5. The figure below shows three possible patterns of dispersion in a population. Describe each pattern in the spaces provided.

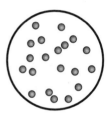

Pattern a.

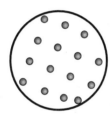

Pattern b.

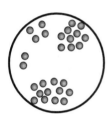

Pattern c.

a. Pattern a. _____

_____

b. Pattern b. _____

_____

c. Pattern c. _____

_____

Circle the letter of the word or phrase that best completes the statement.

6. The patterns of dispersion illustrated in the diagram above are similar in that they all reflect interactions between

   a. the population and its environment.
   b. producers and consumers.
   c. a population and its members.
   d. Both (a) and (b)

CHAPTER

(16) ACTIVE READING

Populations

▶ Section 16-2: How Populations Evolve

Read the passage below, which is reproduced from page 346 of your textbook. Answer the questions that follow.

In 1908, the English mathematician G. H. Hardy and the German physician Wilhelm Weinberg independently demonstrated that dominant alleles do not automatically replace recessive alleles. Using algebra and a simple application of the theories of probability, they showed that the frequency of alleles in a population and the ratio of heterozygous individuals to homozygous individuals does not change from generation to generation unless the population is acted on by other processes that favor particular alleles. Their discovery, called the **Hardy-Weinberg principle,** states that the frequencies of alleles in a population do not change unless evolutionary forces act on the population.

The Hardy-Weinberg principle holds true for any population as long as the population is large enough that its members are not likely to mate with relatives and as long as evolutionary forces are not acting. There are five principal evolutionary forces: mutation, gene flow, nonrandom mating, genetic drift, and natural selection. These evolutionary forces can cause the ratios of genotypes in a population to differ significantly from those predicted by the Hardy-Weinberg principle.

Read each question and write your answer in the space provided.

SKILL: Reading Effectively

1. What did Hardy and Weinberg independently demonstrate in 1908?

_____

_____

2. According to the *Hardy-Weinberg principle*, what causes a change in the frequencies of alleles in a population?

_____

_____

3. What are the five principal evolutionary forces?

_____

_____

4. What effect do these evolutionary forces have on the ratio of heterozygous and homozygous individuals in a population?

_____

_____

5. How can the population size cause a change in the frequencies of alleles in the population?

_____

_____

Circle the letter of the word or phrase that best completes the statement.

6. In forming their theories, Hardy and Weinberg used
   a. simple algebra.
   b. theories of probability.
   c. analytic geometry.
   d. Both (a) and (b)

Ecosystems

▶ Section 17-1: What Is an Ecosystem?

Read the passage below, which is reproduced from page 360 of your textbook. Answer the questions that follow.

> **Ecology** is the study of the interactions of living organisms with one another and with their physical environment. The place where a particular population of a species lives is a **habitat.** The many different species that live together in a habitat are called a **community.** An **ecosystem,** or ecological system, consists of a community and all the physical aspects of its habitat, such as the soil, water, and weather. The physical aspects of a habitat are called **abiotic factors,** and the living organisms in a habitat are called **biotic factors.** The number of species living within an ecosystem is a measure of its **biodiversity.**

Read each question and write your answer in the space provided.

SKILL: Reading Effectively

1. Which word or phrase from the passage above is being described?

   a. _____ all living organisms in a habitat

   b. _____ number of species living within an ecosystem

   c. _____ study of a habitat's abiotic and biotic factors

   d. _____ deer, squirrels, and rabbits living together in a forest form this

   e. _____ an ecological system

   f. _____ soil, water, and weather are examples of these

   g. _____ place where a population lives

   h. _____ all species of freshwater fish that live together in a lake form this

   i. _____ consists of a community and abiotic factors

An analogy is a comparison. Circle the letter of the word that best completes the analogy.

2. Biotic is to bird as abiotic is to

   a. grass.   **c.** nest.

   b. tree.   **d.** worm.

Name _____ Date _____ Class _____

Ecosystems

▶ Section 17-2: Energy Flow in Ecosystems

Read the passage below, which is reproduced from page 365 of your textbook. Answer the questions that follow.

Ecologists study how energy moves through an ecosystem by assigning organisms in that ecosystem to a specific level, called a **trophic level,** based on the organism's source of energy. The path of energy through the trophic levels of an ecosystem is called a **food chain.** The lowest trophic level of any ecosystem is occupied by the producers. Producers such as plants, algae, and bacteria, use the energy of the sun to build energy-rich carbohydrates. Many producers also absorb nitrogen gas and other key substances from the environment and incorporate them into their biological molecules.

At the second trophic level are **herbivores,** animals that eat plants and other primary producers. They are primary consumers. Cows and horses are herbivores, as are caterpillars and some ducks. A herbivore must be able to break down a plant's cellulose molecules into usable compounds.

At the third trophic level are secondary consumers called **carnivores,** animals that eat herbivores. Tigers, wolves, and snakes are carnivores. Some animals, such as bears, and humans are both herbivores and carnivores; and are called **omnivores.** They use simple sugars and starches stored in plants as food, but they cannot digest cellulose.

Read each question and write your answer in the space provided.

SKILL: Reading Effectively

1. What relationship exists between *trophic levels* and a *food chain*?

   _____

   _____

2. What group of organisms occupies the first *trophic level* of an ecosystem?

   _____

   _____

3. What group of organisms occupies the second *trophic level* of an ecosystem?

_____

_____

4. What group of organisms occupies the third *trophic level* of an ecosystem?

_____

_____

5. How are *omnivores* similar to *carnivores*? How do they differ?

_____

_____

SKILL: Sequencing Information

6. Complete each statement by writing the correct number in the space provided. Write *1* if the phrase describes the first trophic level, write *2* if the phrase describes the second trophic level, or write *3* if the phrase describes the third trophic level.

a. _____ Primary consumers are found here.

b. _____ Organisms here use the energy of the sun to build energy-rich carbohydrates.

c. _____ Tigers, wolves, and snakes are found here.

d. _____ Organisms here are capable of breaking down cellulose.

e. _____ Secondary consumers are found here.

f. _____ Plants, algae, and bacteria are found here.

g. _____ Humans are found here.

h. _____ Organisms here break down a plant's molecules into usable compounds.

Circle the letter of the word or phrase that best completes the statement.

7. All of the following are examples of primary consumers EXCEPT
    a. maple trees.
    b. caterpillars.
    c. cows.
    d. horses.

Ecosystems

▶ Section 17-3: Ecosystems Cycle Materials

Read the passage below, which is reproduced from page 371 of your textbook. Answer the questions that follow.

In the nonliving portion of the water cycle, water vapor in the atmosphere condenses and falls to the Earth's surface as rain or snow. Some of this water seeps into the soil and becomes part of the **ground water,** which is water retained beneath the surface of Earth. Most of the remaining water that falls to the Earth does not stay at the surface. Instead, heated by the sun, it reenters the atmosphere by evaporation.

In the living portion of the water cycle, much water is taken up by the roots of plants. After passing through a plant, the water moves into the atmosphere by evaporating from the leaves, a process called **transpiration.** Transpiration is also a sun-driven process. The sun heats the Earth's atmosphere, creating wind currents that draw moisture from the tiny openings in the leaves of plants.

Read each question and write your answer in the space provided.

SKILL: Reading Effectively

1. What occurs in the nonliving part of the water cycle?

_____

_____

2. What happens to this precipitation?

_____

_____

3. What occurs in the living part of the water cycle?

_____

_____

4. What is *transpiration*?

_____

_____

5. Why is *transpiration* classified as a "sun-driven process"?

_____

_____

SKILL: Interpreting Graphics

6. The figure below shows the water cycle. Insert the following terms in the correct spaces: evaporation, ground water, precipitation, transpiration, and water vapor.

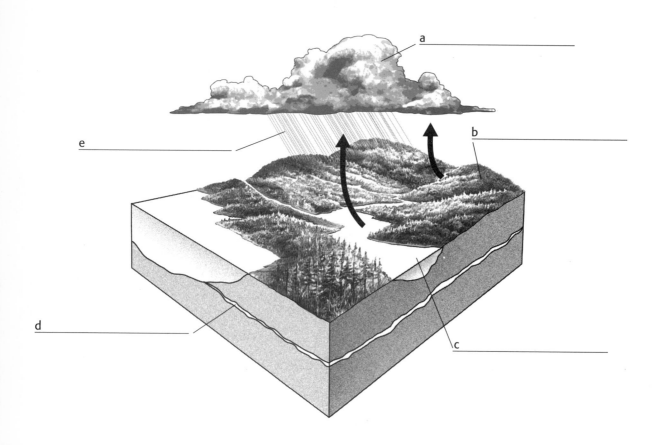

Circle the letter of the word that best completes the statement.

7. Water retained beneath Earth's surface is called
   a. precipitation.
   b. transpiration.
   c. condensation.
   d. ground water.

CHAPTER
18 ACTIVE READING

Biological Communities

▶ Section 18-1: How Organisms Interact in Communities

Read the passage below, which is reproduced from page 384 of your textbook. Answer the questions that follow.

In **symbiosis,** two or more species live together in a close, long-term association. Symbiotic relationships can be beneficial to both organisms or may benefit one organism and leave the other harmed or unaffected. **Parasitism** is one type of symbiotic relationship that is detrimental to, or harms, the host organism. In this relationship, one organism feeds on and usually lives in another, typically larger, organism. **Mutualism** is a symbiotic relationship in which both participating species benefit. A well-known instance of mutualism involves ants and aphids. The ants feed on fluid the aphids secrete, and in exchange, the ants protect the aphids from insect predators. A third form of symbiosis is **commensalism,** a symbiotic relationship in which one species benefits and the other is neither harmed nor helped. Among the best-known examples of commensalism are the feeding and protection relationships between certain small tropical fishes and sea anemones, marine animals that have stinging tentacles.

Read each question and write your answer in the space provided.

SKILL: Reading Effectively

1. Write *P* if the phrase describes parasitism, *M* if it describes mutualism, or write *C* if it describes commensalism. Some responses will have more than one letter.

   a. _____ exists between certain tropical fish and sea anemones

   b. _____ type of symbiotic relationship

   c. _____ the host organism is harmed

   d. _____ one species is neither harmed nor helped

   e. _____ at least one species benefits

Circle the letter of the phrase that best completes the statement.

2. Mutualism is a symbiotic relationship in which
   a. both species are harmed.   c. one species is harmed.
   b. neither species benefits.   d. both species benefit.

Biological Communities

▶ Section 18-2: How Competition Shapes Communities

Read the passage below, which is reproduced from page 390 of your textbook. Answer the questions that follow.

A key investigation carried out in the early 1990s by David Tilman of the University of Minnesota illustrates the relationship between **biodiversity,** which is the variety of living organisms present in a community, and productivity. Tilman, along with co-workers and students, tended 147 experimental plots in a Minnesota prairie. Each plot contained a mix of up to 24 native prairie plant species. The biologist monitored the plots, measuring how much growth was occurring. Tilman found that the more species a plot had, the greater the amount of plant material produced in that plot. Tilman's experiments clearly demonstrated that increased biodiversity leads to greater productivity. Tilman also found that the plots with greater numbers of species recovered more fully from a major drought. Thus, the biologically diverse plots were also more stable than the plots with fewer species.

Read each question and write your answer in the space provided.

SKILL: Reading Effectively

1. What sentence expresses the main idea of the passage? What is the main idea?

_____

_____

_____

2. What was the location and focus of Tilman's investigation?

_____

_____

Circle the letter of the phrase that best completes the statement.

3. According to the passage, the greater the variety of living organisms present in a community, the greater the

   a. size of the community.
   b. stability of the community.
   c. amount of plant material used by the community.
   d. Both (a) and (b)

Biological Communities

▶ Section 18-3: Major Biological Communities

Read the passage below, which is reproduced from page 392 of your textbook. Answer the questions that follow.

A major biological community that occurs over a large area of land is called a **biome.** A biome's structure and appearance are similar throughout its geographic distribution. While there are different ways of classifying biomes, the classification system used here recognizes seven widely occurring biomes: tropical rain forest, desert, savanna, temperate deciduous forest, temperate grassland, taiga, and tundra. These biomes differ greatly from one another because they have developed in regions with very different climates.

In general, temperature and available moisture decrease as latitude (distance from the equator) increases. They also decrease as elevation (height above sea level) increases.

Read each question and write your answer in the space provided.

SKILL: Reading Effectively

1. What Key Term is defined in the opening sentence of this passage?

_____

2. According to the classification system used by this text, what seven *biomes* occur on Earth?

_____

_____

_____

3. What happens to temperature and available moisture as elevation increases?

_____

_____

Circle the letter of the phrase that best answers the question.

4. What occurs as latitude decreases?
   a. Temperature increases.
   b. Available moisture increases.
   c. Elevation decreases.
   d. both (a) and (b)

CHAPTER
(19) ACTIVE READING

Human Impact on the Environment

▶ Section 19-1: Global Change

Read the passage below, which is reproduced from page 406 of your textbook. Answer the questions that follow.

Acid rain forms when coal-burning power plants send smoke high into the atmosphere through smokestacks that are more than 65 m (210 ft) tall. This smoke contains high concentrations of sulfur because the coal that plants burn is rich in sulfur. The intent of those who designed the power plants was to release the sulfur-rich smoke high into the atmosphere, where winds would disperse and dilute it.

Scientists have discovered that the sulfur introduced into the atmosphere by smokestacks combines with water vapor to produce sulfuric acid. Rain and snow carry the sulfuric acid back to Earth's surface. This acidified precipitation is **acid rain.**

Read each question and write your answer in the space provided.

SKILL: Recognizing Cause and Effect

1. What are the cause and effect of the relationship described in the second sentence of this passage?

_____

_____

2. Why did power plant designers build 65 m tall smokestacks?

_____

_____

3. What actually occurs when the sulfur-rich smoke is released into the atmosphere?

_____

_____

4. What causes the sulfuric acid to reach Earth's surface?

_____

_____

5. In the spaces provided, sequence the events below to show how acid rain forms. Write *1* in front of the event that occurs first, write *2* to show what happens next, and so on.

a. _____ Sulfur-rich smoke is released into the atmosphere.

b. _____ Acidified precipitation falls to earth.

c. _____ Smoke containing high concentrations of sulfur is produced.

d. _____ Sulfur combines with water vapor to produce sulfuric acid.

e. _____ Coal is burned in power plants.

Circle the letter of the phrase that best completes the statement.

6. Acid rain is an effect of
   a. wind currents.
   b. burning of coal.
   c. evaporation of water.
   d. Both (a) and (b)

CHAPTER

(19) ACTIVE READING

Human Impact on the Environment

▶ Section 19-2: Ecosystem Damage

Read the passage below, which is reproduced from page 415 of your textbook. Answer the questions that follow.

The world's population exceeded 6 billion in early 1999, and the annual increase is now about 94 million people. About 260,000 people are added to the world's population each day, or about 180 people every minute. Population growth is fastest in the developing countries of Asia, Africa, and Latin America. Growth is slowest in the industrialized countries of North America, Europe, Japan, New Zealand, and Australia. The population growth in the United States is only 0.8 percent, less than half of the global rate. Most European countries are growing even more slowly, and the populations of Germany and Russia are actually declining. In contrast, as of 1996, Nigeria's population was increasing by about 3.05 percent per year.

Read each question and write your answer in the space provided.

SKILL: Reading Effectively

1. What does the word *about* in the first sentence indicate about the world's annual rate of population growth?

_____

_____

2. About how many people are added to the world's population during one of your biology classes?

_____

_____

3. Where is population growth the fastest?

_____

_____

4. Where is population growth the slowest?

_____

_____

5. Based on the passage, how could you determine the world's population growth rate?

_____

_____

_____

Circle the letter of the phrase that best completes the statement.

6. The population growth rate in most European countries is

    a. less than 0.8 percent.
    b. about 0.8 percent.
    c. more than 1.6 percent.
    d. more than 3.05 percent.

CHAPTER

19 **ACTIVE READING**

Human Impact on the Environment

▶ Section 19-3: Solving Environmental Problems

Read the passage below, which is reproduced from page 418 of your textbook. Answer the questions that follow.

There are five components to successfully solving any environmental problem.

Assessment: The first stage is scientific analysis of the problem, the gathering of information about what is happening. To construct a model of the ecosystem, data must be collected and experiments must be performed. A model makes it possible to describe how the ecosystem is responding to the situation. It is then used to make predictions about the future course of the ecosystem.

Risk analysis: Using the information obtained by scientific analysis, it is possible to predict the consequences of environmental intervention, that is, what could be expected to happen if a particular course of action were followed. It is also necessary to evaluate any adverse effects that a plan of action might cause.

Public education: When a clear choice can be made among alternative courses of action, the public must be informed. This involves explaining the problem in understandable terms, presenting the alternative actions available, and explaining the probable costs and results of the different choices.

Political action: The public, through its elected officials, selects and implements a course of action. Individuals can be influential at this stage by exercising their right to vote and by contacting their elected officials.

Follow-through: The results of any action should be carefully monitored to see if the environmental problem is being solved.

Read each question and write your answer in the space provided.

SKILL: Reading Effectively

1. What type of information is gathered during a scientific analysis of the problem?

_____

_____

2. How does a model of the ecosystem help assess the problem?

_____

_____

_____

3. What three actions are involved in public education?

_____

_____

_____

4. How can individuals influence selection of a specific course of action?

_____

_____

_____

SKILL: Sequencing Information

5. Order the statements below to show the sequence of actions taken to success-fully solve an environmental problem. In the spaces provided, write _1_ in front of the event that occurs first, write _2_ to show what happens next, and so on.

a. _____ Actions are taken to resolve the problem.

b. _____ A model of the ecosystem is made.

c. _____ The ecosystem is monitored to see if the action has solved the problem.

d. _____ Information about the problem and possible action is presented to the public.

e. _____ Data is collected, and experiments are conducted.

f. _____ Predictions are made about the consequences of environmental intervention.

g. _____ Based on a model, predictions are made about the future course of the ecosystem.

Circle the letter of the word or phrase that best completes the statement.

6. A model of an ecosystem is based on
    a. data collected from the ecosystem.   **c.** public opinion.
    b. experiments.   **d.** Both (a) and (b)

Introduction to the Kingdoms of Life

► Section 20-1: Simple Unicellular Organisms

Read the passage below, which is reproduced from page 432 of your textbook. Answer the questions that follow.

Biologists have organized living things into six large groups called kingdoms. Kingdoms are the largest taxonomic group of organisms and include several related phyla. Biologists group organisms in the different kingdoms based on their similarities. Most biologists use the six-kingdom system. The characteristics of these six kingdoms are summarized in the table below.

Characteristics	Kingdom					
	Eubacteria	Archaebacteria	Protista	Fungi	Plantae	Animalia
Cell type	Prokaryote	Prokaryote	Eukaryote	Eukaryote	Eukaryote	Eukaryote
Cell structure	Cell wall, peptidoglycan	Cell wall, no peptidoglycan	Mixed	Cell wall, chitin	Cell wall	No cell wall
Body type	Unicellular	Unicellular	Unicellular, multicellular	Unicellular, multicellular	Multicellular	Multicellular
Nutrition	Autotrophic and heterotrophic	Autotrophic and heterotrophic	Autotrophic and heterotrophic	Heterotrophic	Autotrophic	Heterotrophic

Read each question and write your answer in the space provided.

SKILL: Reading Effectively

1. What is a kingdom?

_____

_____

2. What are the names of the six kingdoms?

_____

_____

_____

3. How are organisms grouped in the different kingdoms?

_____

_____

4. What characteristics of each kingdom are identified in the table?

_____

_____

5. In which kingdom(s) would you find eukaryotes?

_____

_____

6. In which kingdom(s) would you find unicellular organisms?

_____

_____

7. In which kingdom(s) would you find autotrophs?

_____

_____

8. Which kingdom is made up entirely of organisms lacking a cell wall?

_____

_____

9. How are members of kingdoms Fungi and Animalia alike? How do they differ?

_____

_____

_____

_____

10. How are members of kingdoms Archaebacteria and Plantae alike? How do they differ?

_____

_____

_____

_____

Circle the letter of the word that best completes the statement.

11. Eubacteria is to peptidoglycan as Fungi is to
   a. autotroph.
   b. multicellular.
   c. eukaryote.
   d. chitin.

Introduction to the Kingdoms of Life

► Section 20-2: Advent of Multicellularity

Read the passage below, which is reproduced from page 436 of your textbook. Answer the questions that follow.

Occasionally, the cell walls of bacteria adhere to one another. In fact, some bacteria, such as cyanobacteria, form filaments, sheets, or three-dimensional formations of cells. However, these formations cannot be considered truly multicellular because few cell activities are coordinated. Such bacteria may properly be considered colonial (living together). A **colonial organism** is a group of cells that are permanently associated but that do not communicate with one another.

An **aggregation** is a temporary collection of cells that come together for a period of time and then separate. For example, a plasmodial slime mold is a unicellular organism that spends most of its life moving about and feeding as a single-celled amoeba. When starved, however, these cells aggregate into a large group. This weblike mass produces spores which are dispersed.

Read each question and write your answer in the space provided.

SKILL: Reading Effectively

1. What is a *colonial organism*?

_____

_____

2. Why are cyanobacteria adhering together in a three-dimensional formation of cells not considered to be multicellular?

_____

_____

Circle the letter of the phrase that best completes the statement.

3. Colonial organisms and aggregates differ in the
  a. manner in which the cells communicate with each other.
  b. number of cells joined together.
  c. duration of cell association.
  d. manner in which the cells reproduce.

CHAPTER
20 ACTIVE READING

Introduction to the Kingdoms of Life

▶ Section 20-3: Kingdoms of Plants and Animals

Read the passage below, which is reproduced from page 443 of your textbook. Answer the questions that follow.

Animals are multicellular heterotrophs whose cells lack a cell wall, are organized as tissues, are mostly diploid, and whose zygotes develop through several stages. Most animals reproduce sexually. In animals, cells formed in meiosis function directly as gametes. The haploid cells do not divide by mitosis first, as they do in plants and fungi, but rather fuse directly with one another to form the zygote. The zygote then gradually develops into an adult by going through several developmental stages.

Specialized tissue called muscle enables animals to move on their own. Movement enables animals to avoid predators and to look for food and mates. A remarkable form of movement unique to animals is flying, an ability that is well developed among some insects and vertebrates.

Read each question and write your answer in the space provided.

SKILL: Reading Effectively

1. What six characteristics of animals are identified in the first sentence of this passage?

   _____

   _____

   _____

2. What causes animals to be able to move on their own?

   _____

   _____

Circle the letter of the word or phrase that best completes the statement.

3. Flying is a form of movement that is well developed among
   a. vertebrates.   c. amphibians.
   b. insects.   d. Both (a) and (b)

CHAPTER
21 **ACTIVE READING**

—Viruses and Bacteria

▶ Section 21-1: Viruses

Read the passage below, which is reproduced from page 454 of your textbook. Answer the questions that follow.

Viruses cause damage when the viruses replicate inside the cells. The entry of the virus into the cell is not by itself harmful, but after the virus has replicated itself several hundred times and breaks out, the cell is destroyed. Organ damage in an organism can become severe if enough tissue is damaged by the virus. Any agent that causes disease is called a **pathogen.**

The cycle of viral infection, replication, and cell destruction is called the **lytic cycle.** After the viral genes have entered the cell, they use the host cell to replicate viral genes and to make viral proteins, such as capsids. The proteins are then assembled with the replicated viral genes to form complete viruses. The host cell is broken open and releases newly made viruses.

During an infection, some viruses stay inside the cells but do not make new viruses. Instead of producing virus particles, the viral gene is inserted into the host chromosome and is called a **provirus.** Whenever the cell divides, the provirus also divides, resulting in two infected host cells. In this cycle, called the **lysogenic cycle,** the viral genome replicates without destroying the host cell.

Read each question and write your answer in the space provided.

SKILL: Reading Effectively

1. How do viruses damage a cell?

_____

_____

2. What relationship exists between viruses and *pathogens*?

_____

_____

3. What sentence expresses the main idea of the second paragraph?

_____

_____

4. The figure below shows the lytic and lysogenic cycles. In the spaces provided, describe what is occurring in each numbered part of the figure.

Lytic Cycle   **Lysogenic Cycle**

Part 1

Part 5

Part 2

Part 4

Part 3

a. Part 1: _____

_____

b. Part 2: _____

_____

c. Part 3: _____

_____

d. Part 4: _____

_____

e. Part 5: _____

_____

Circle the letter of the phrase that best completes the statement.

5. Viruses cause damage when they
   a. invade cells.
   b. replicate inside cells.
   c. remain inside a host cell.
   d. Both (a) and (b)

─Viruses and Bacteria

▶ **Section 21-2: Bacteria**

Read the passage below, which is reproduced from page 460 of your textbook. Answer the questions that follow.

Bacteria, which outnumber all eukaryotes combined, differ from eukaryotes in at least seven ways.

Internal compartmentalization: Bacteria are prokaryotes. Unlike eukaryotes, prokaryotes lack a cell nucleus. Bacterial cells have no internal compartments or membrane systems.

Cell size: Most bacterial cells are about 1 μm in diameter; most eukaryotic cells are 10 times that size.

Multicellularity: All bacteria are single cells. Some bacteria may stick together or may form strands. However, these formations are not truly multicellular because the cytoplasm in the cells does not directly interconnect, as is the case with many multicellular eukaryotes. Also, the activities of the cells are not specialized.

Chromosomes: Bacterial chromosomes consist of a single circular piece of DNA. Eukaryotic chromosomes are linear pieces of DNA that are associated with proteins.

Reproduction: Bacteria reproduce by binary fission, a process in which one cell pinches into two cells. In eukaryotes, however, microtubules pull chromosomes to opposite poles of the cell during mitosis. Afterward, the cytoplasm of the eukaryotic cell divides in half, forming two cells.

Flagella: Bacterial flagella are simple structures composed of a single fiber of protein that spins like a corkscrew to move the cell. Eukaryotic flagella are more-complex structures made of microtubules that whip back and forth rather than spin. Some bacteria also have shorter, thicker outgrowths called **pili** that attach to surfaces or to other cells.

Metabolic diversity: Bacteria have many metabolic abilities that eukaryotes lack. For example, bacteria perform several different kinds of anaerobic and aerobic processes, while eukaryotes are mostly aerobic organisms.

(continued on the next page)

Read each question, and write your answer in the space provided.

SKILL: Organizing Information

1. Write *B* if the statement describes bacteria or *E* if the statement describes eukaryotes.

   a. _____ reproduce by binary fission

   b. _____ lack a cell nucleus

   c. _____ chromosomes are linear pieces of DNA

   d. _____ activities of the cell are specialized

   e. _____ cytoplasm lacks membrane systems

   f. _____ mostly aerobic organisms

   g. _____ most cells are about 1 μm in diameter

   h. _____ single cells

   i. _____ cytoplasm contains internal compartments

   j. _____ single fiber flagella spin like a corkscrew

   k. _____ activities of the cell are not specialized

   l. _____ flagella are complex structures made of microtubules

   m. _____ multicellular

   n. _____ during cell division, microtubules pull chromosomes to opposite poles

   o. _____ cytoplasm lacks internal compartments

   p. _____ cytoplasm of cells forming a strand does not directly interconnect

   q. _____ perform different kinds of anaerobic and aerobic respiration

   r. _____ two new cells form when cytoplasm divides in half

   s. _____ may have pili

   t. _____ chromosomes consist of a single circular piece of DNA

Circle the letter of the phrase that best completes the statement.

2. Most bacterial cells are
   a. 10 times larger than an average eukaryotic cell.
   b. as large as an average eukaryotic cell.
   c. one-tenth the size of an average eukaryotic cell.
   d. double the size of an average eukaryotic cell.

CHAPTER
(22) ACTIVE READING

●— Protists

▶ Section 22-1: Characteristics of Protists

Read the passage below, which is reproduced from page 480 of your textbook. Answer the questions that follow.

Reproduction in the unicellular green alga *Chlamydomonas* is typical of unicellular protists. *Chlamydomonas* species reproduce sexually and asexually.

As mature organisms, these single-celled protists are haploid. When they reproduce asexually, *Chlamydomonas* species divide by mitosis, producing haploid cells called zoospores, which remain within the wall of the parent cell. Mature zoospores break out of the parent cell and grow to become mature haploid cells.

During environmental stress, such as a shortage of nutrients, *Chlamydomonas* species reproduce sexually. The haploid cell divides first by mitosis to produce haploid gametes. After those gametes are released, a pair of gametes from different *Chlamydomonas* individuals fuse to form a pair. Each gamete sheds its cell walls. Then the gametes fuse into a diploid zygote with a thick protective wall called a **zygospore.** A zygospore can withstand unfavorable environmental conditions for long periods of time. When environmental conditions become favorable again, meiosis within the zygospore produces haploid cells, which break out of the zygospore wall. These haploid cells grow into mature cells, completing the sexual life cycle.

Read each question and write your answer in the space provided.

SKILL: Reading Effectively

1. How do most unicellular protists reproduce?

_____

_____

2. How do *Chlamydomonas* species produce zoospores?

_____

_____

3. What causes *Chlamydomonas* species to reproduce sexually?

_____

_____

4. How does a *zygospore* form?

_____

_____

_____

_____

SKILL: Interpreting Graphics

5. The figure below shows *Chlamydomonas* reproduction. In the spaces provided, insert the following labels on the figure: gametes, mature cell, meiosis, mitosis, zoospores, and zygote. One label will be used more than once. One example is given for you.

Sexual Reproduction   **Asexual Reproduction**

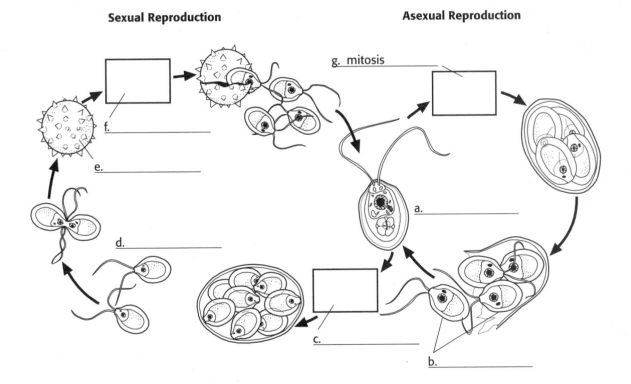

g. mitosis

f. _____

e. _____

d. _____

a. _____

b. _____

c. _____

Circle the letter of the word or phrase that best answers the question.

6. Which of the following is part of both asexual and sexual reproduction of *Chlamydomonas*?

   a. production of gametes
   b. meiosis
   c. zoospores remain inside parent cell
   d. mitosis

CHAPTER
22 ACTIVE READING

Protists

▶ Section 22-2: Protist Diversity

Read the passage below, which is reproduced from page 482 of your textbook. Answer the questions that follow.

Amoebas, members of the phylum Rhizopoda, are protists that move using flexible, cytoplasmic extensions. These extensions are called **pseudopodia,** from the Greek words *pseudo,* meaning "false," and *podium,* meaning "foot." Because an amoeba has no cell walls or flagella, it is extremely flexible. A pseudopodium bulges from the cell surface, stretches outward, and anchors itself to a nearby surface. The cytoplasm from the rest of the amoeba then flows into the pseudopodium. Pseudopodia can surround and engulf food particles. Amoebas live in both fresh water and salt water and are especially abundant in soil. Meiosis and sexual reproduction do not occur in amoebas. They reproduce by fission, dividing into two new cells.

Read each question and write your answer in the space provided.

SKILL: Reading Effectively

1. What Key Term is defined in the first sentence? What is the meaning of this term?

   _____

   _____

2. How does knowing the meaning of the Greek words *pseudo* and *podium* help define the Key Term *pseudopodium*?

   _____

   _____

3. What causes an *amoeba* to be so flexible?

   _____

   _____

Circle the letter of the word or phrase that best completes the statement.

4. Amoeba are capable of all of the following EXCEPT
   a. fission.   c. engulfing food particles.
   b. meiosis.   d. moving by pseudopods.

CHAPTER
22 **ACTIVE READING**

—**Protists**

▶ Section 22-3: Protists and Health

Read the passage below, which is reproduced from page 491 of your textbook. Answer the questions that follow.

Malaria is caused by several species of *Plasmodium* and is spread by the bite of certain mosquitoes. There are three stages in the *Plasmodium* life cycle. When an infected mosquito bites a human to obtain blood, it injects saliva that contains a chemical that prevents the blood from clotting. If the mosquito is infected with *Plasmodium*, it will also inject about 1,000 protists with its saliva. This stage of *Plasmodium* is called the **sporozoite.** Sporozoites infect the liver, where they rapidly divide and produce millions of cells of the second stage of the life cycle, called the **merozoite.** Merozoites infect red blood cells and divide rapidly. In about 48 hours the blood cells rupture, releasing more merozoites and toxic substances. This begins a cycle of fever and chills that characterizes malaria. The cycle repeats itself every 48–72 hours as new waves of blood cells are infected and destroyed. In the third stage, some of the merozoites in the blood develop into gametes. After these gametes are eaten by a mosquito, they form a zygote. Eventually many infectious sporozoites are formed in the zygote and migrate to the salivary glands of the mosquito.

Read each question and write your answer in the space provided.

SKILL: Organizing Information

1. Summarize the key events that make up each stage in the *Plasmodium* life cycle.

   a. Stage 1: _____

   _____

   _____

   b. Stage 2: _____

   _____

   _____

   _____

c. Stage 3: _____

_____

_____

_____

An analogy is a comparison. Circle the letter of the word or phrase that best completes the analogy.

2. Sporozoites are to the liver as merozoites are to
   a. red blood cells.
   b. stomach.
   c. saliva.
   d. white blood cells.

CHAPTER
23 **ACTIVE READING**

Fungi

▶ Section 23-1: Characteristics of Fungi

Read the passage below, which is reproduced from page 500 of your textbook. Answer the questions that follow.

Traditionally, biologists grouped fungi with plants because fungi are immobile, have a cell wall, and appear "rooted" in the soil. However, the unique features of fungi indicate that they are not closely related to any other group of organisms.

Fungi are heterotrophic: Plants appear green because they contain chlorophyll, the pigment that aids in photosynthesis. Fungi do not appear green because they do not contain chlorophyll. For example, the stalk and cap of the mushroom are not green like the stem and leaves of a plant. Because fungi are heterotrophs, they obtain energy by breaking down organic molecules that they absorb from their environment.

Fungi have filamentous bodies: Plants are made of many cell and tissue types, but fungi are made of long, slender filaments. These filaments weave tightly together to form the fungus body and reproductive structures.

Fungal cells contain chitin: The cells of mushrooms, like the cells of all fungi, have walls made of **chitin,** the tough polysaccharide found in the hard outer covering of insects. Plant cells have walls made of cellulose, a different polysaccharide.

Fungi exhibit nuclear mitosis: Mitosis in fungi is different from mitosis in plants and most other eukaryotes. In most eukaryotes, the nuclear envelope disintegrates in prophase and re-forms in telophase. In dividing mushroom cells, however, the nuclear envelope remains intact from prophase to anaphase. As a result, spindle fibers form within the nucleus. The spindle fibers then drag chromosomes to opposite poles of the nucleus rather than to opposite poles of the cell. Mitosis is complete when the nuclear envelope pinches in two.

Read each question and write your answer in the space provided.

SKILL: Reading Effectively

1. In the past, why did biologists classify fungi with plants?

_____

_____

2. Why does a mushroom lack the green coloring found in plants?

_____

_____

3. How do fungi obtain the energy needed to carry out life processes?

_____

_____

4. How does mitosis in fungi differ from that in plants and most other eukaryotes?

_____

_____

SKILL: Recognizing Similarities and Differences

5. In the spaces provided, write *P* if the statement describes plants, write *F* if the statement describes fungi, or write *B* if the statement describes both plants and fungi.

a. _____ made of long, slender filaments

b. _____ lack chlorophyll

c. _____ mitosis occurs in the organism

d. _____ autotrophs

e. _____ cells walls contain chitin

f. _____ need energy to carry out life processes

g. _____ cell walls contain cellulose

h. _____ made of many cell and tissue types

i. _____ immobile

j. _____ spindle fibers form within the nucleus

Circle the letter of the word or phrase that best answers the question.

6. Which of the following is a trait shared by fungi and plants?
   a. exhibit nuclear mitosis
   b. cell walls contain a polysaccharide
   c. heterotrophic
   d. contain a variety of tissue types

CHAPTER
(23) ACTIVE READING

——Fungi

▶ Section 23-2: Fungal Diversity

Read the passage below, which is reproduced from page 504 of your textbook. Answer the questions that follow.

If you place an uncovered loaf of bread near a windowsill, after a few days a cottony mold will cover its surface. This common black bread mold is *Rhizopus stolonifer*, a member of the phylum Zygomycota. Members of the phylum Zygomycota are named for the thick-walled sexual structures called **zygosporangia** that characterize the phylum's members. Species of *Rhizopus* and other zygomycetes usually live in the soil and feed on decaying plant and animal matter. The mycelia that grow along the surface of bread are called **stolons**. The hyphae that anchor the fungus in the bread are called **rhizoids**.

Asexual reproduction in zygomycetes is much more common than sexual reproduction. During asexual reproduction, haploid spores are produced in the tips of specialized hyphae. When these spores mature, they are shed and are carried by the wind to new locations, where they germinate and start new mycelia.

Read each question and write your answer in the space provided.

SKILL: Sequencing Information

1. Sequence the statements to show what occurs during asexual reproduction in zygomycetes. Write *1* in front of the event that occurs first, write *2* to show what happens next, and so on.

   a. _____ Wind carries spores to new locations.

   b. _____ New mycelia are produced.

   c. _____ Specialized hyphae produce haploid spores.

   d. _____ Spores germinate.

   e. _____ Mature spores are shed.

An analogy is a comparison. Circle the letter of the word or phrase that best completes the analogy.

2. Rhizoids are to hyphae as stolons are to
   a. cell walls.   c. spores.
   b. mycelia.   d. mold.

Fungi

▶ Section 23-3: Fungal Partnerships

Read the passage below, which is reproduced from page 509 of your textbook. Answer the questions that follow.

A **lichen** is a symbiosis between a fungus and a photosynthetic partner such as a green alga, a cyanobacterium, or both. The photosynthetic partner provides carbohydrates. It is protected from the environment by the fungal partner, which provides it with mineral nutrients. In most lichens, the fungi is an ascomycete. When you look at a lichen, you are seeing the fungus. The photosynthetic partner is hidden between layers of hyphae. Sunlight penetrates the layers of hyphae and enables photosynthesis. The tough construction of the fungus combined with the photosynthetic abilities of the alga have enabled lichens to colonize harsh habitats. Lichens have been found in arid desert regions and in the Arctic; lichens grow on bare soil, on tree trunks, and on sun-baked rocks. During succession, lichens are often the first colonists. They break down rocks and prepare the environment for other organisms. Lichens are a key component of primary succession because they are able to carry out nitrogen fixation.

Read each question and write your answer in the space provided.

SKILL: Recognizing Cause and Effect

1. Two independent events can be linked in a cause-and-effect relationship. The first event to occur, or the cause, triggers a second event, or the effect, to happen. In the spaces below, identify and write the missing part of each cause-and-effect relationship.

   a. Cause: Sunlight penetrates layers of hyphae.

   Effect: _____

   b. Cause: _____

   Effect: Lichens are able to survive harsh environments.

Circle the letter of the phrase that best completes the statement.

2. In a lichen, the fungal partner

   a. protects the photosynthetic partner.
   b. supplies the photosynthetic partner with mineral nutrients.
   c. provides the photosynthetic partner with carbohydrates.
   d. Both (a) and (b)

CHAPTER

24 **ACTIVE READING**

Introduction to Plants

▶ Section 24-1: Adaptations of Plants

Read the passage below, which is reproduced from page 522 of your textbook. Answer the questions that follow.

After vascular tissue, the next great adaptation to appear in plants was the seed. A **seed** is a structure that contains a plant embryo. Most plants living today are **seed plants**—vascular plants that produce seeds. The first seed plants appeared about 380 million years ago. Seeds offer a plant's offspring several survival advantages.

Protection: Seeds are surrounded by a protective cover called the seed coat. The seed coat protects the embryo from drying out and from mechanical injury and disease.

Nourishment: Most kinds of seeds have a supply of organic nutrients stored in them. These nutrients are a ready source of nourishment for the plant embryo as it starts to grow.

Plant dispersal: Seeds disperse (spread) the offspring of seed plants. Many seeds have appendages that help wind, water, or animals carry them away from their parent plant. Dispersal prevents competition for water, nutrients, light, and living space between parents and offspring.

Delayed growth: The embryo in a seed is in a state of suspended animation. Most seeds will not sprout until conditions are favorable, such as when moisture is present and the weather is warm. Thus, seeds make it possible for plant embryos to survive through unfavorable periods, such as droughts or cold winters.

Read each question and write your answer in the space provided.

SKILL: Reading Effectively

1. What Key Terms are defined in the first paragraph? What are their meanings?

_____

_____

2. What is the function of a seed coat?

_____

_____

3. How does a plant embryo obtain the nourishment it needs for growth?

_____

_____

4. How is the meaning of the term *dispersal* indicated in the passage?

_____

_____

5. What are ways that seeds may be dispersed?

_____

_____

6. If seeds were unable to be dispersed, what four items would parents and off-spring compete for?

_____

_____

_____

SKILL: Interpreting Graphics

7. The figure below shows a seed. On the spaces to the left of the figure label the parts of the seed: seed coat, and wing. On the spaces to the right of the figure list two favorable conditions needed for the seed to sprout.

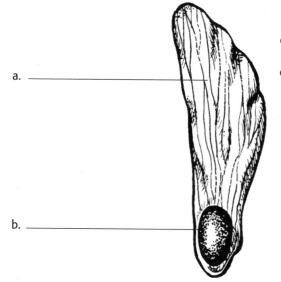

c. _____

d. _____

a. _____

b. _____

Circle the letter of the word or phrase that best answers the question.

8. What was the first adaptation for life on land that appeared in plants?
   a. vascular tissue   **c.** seeds
   b. cell walls   **d.** roots

CHAPTER
(24) ACTIVE READING

Introduction to Plants

▶ Section 24-2: Kinds of Plants

Read the passage below, which is reproduced from page 527 of your textbook. Answer the questions that follow.

The nonvascular plants include the mosses and the two simplest groups of plants—liverworts and hornworts.

Mosses: The mosses (phylum Bryophyta) are the most familiar nonvascular plants. The "leafy" green plants that you recognize as mosses are gametophytes. Moss sporophytes grow from the tip of a gametophyte. Each sporophyte consists of a bare stalk topped by a spore capsule. Most mosses have a cuticle, stomata, and some simple conducting cells. The walls of the water-conducting cells in mosses are not thick like they are in a vascular plant. Mosses never get very large because their water-conducting cells carry water only short distances.

Liverworts: Like the mosses, liverworts (phylum Hepatophyta) grow in mats of many individuals. Liverworts have no conducting cells, no cuticle, and no stomata. Their gametophytes are green. In some species, the gametophytes are flattened and have lobes. Structures that resemble stems and leaves make up the gametophytes of most liverworts, like those of the mosses. The sporophytes of liverworts are very small and consist of a short stalk topped by a spore capsule.

Hornworts: The hornworts (phylum Anthocerophyta) are a small group of bryophytes that, like the liverworts, completely lack conducting cells. Hornworts have both stomata and a cuticle. The gametophyte of a hornwort is green and flattened. Green horn-like sporophytes grow upward from the gametophytes.

Read each question and write your answer in the space provided.

SKILL: **Recognizing Similarities and Differences**

1. Write *M* if the statement describes mosses, write *L* if the statement describes liverworts, or write *H* if the statement describes hornworts. Some statements describe more than one type of nonvascular plant.

    a. _____ belong to phylum Hepatophyta

    b. _____ most familiar nonvascular plants

    c. _____ lack conducting cells

d. _____ belong to phylum Bryophyta

e. _____ may have a cuticle

f. _____ grow in mats of many individuals

g. _____ very small sporophytes

h. _____ have some simple conducting cells

i. _____ belong to phylum Anthocerophyta

j. _____ gametophytes are green

k. _____ water-conducting cells carry water only short distances

l. _____ hornlike sporophytes grow upward from gametophytes

m. _____ sporophyte consists of a bare stalk topped by a spore capsule

n. _____ may have stomata

o. _____ some gametophytes are flattened and have lobes

p. _____ sporophyte consists of short stalk topped by a spore capsule

Circle the letter of the word or phrase that best completes the statement.

2. Structures that resemble stems and leaves make up the gametophytes of most
   a. mosses.
   b. liverworts.
   c. hornworts.
   d. Both (a) and (b)

CHAPTER
24 ACTIVE READING

Introduction to Plants

▶ Section 24-3: Plants in Our Lives

Read the passage below, which is reproduced from page 536 of your textbook. Answer the questions that follow.

Most of the foods that people eat come directly or indirectly from the fruits of **cereals,** which are grasses that are grown as food for humans and livestock. Cereal grasses produce large numbers of a type of edible, dry fruit called a **grain.** A grain contains a single seed with a large supply of endosperm. A grain is covered by a dry, papery husk called the bran, which includes the wall of the ovary and the seed coat. Cereal grains are rich in carbohydrates and also contain protein, vitamins, and dietary fiber. More than 70 percent of the world's culti-vated farmland is used for growing cereal grains. In fact, more than half of the calories that humans consume come from just three species of cereal grasses: wheat, corn, and rice.

Read each question and write your answer in the space provided.

SKILL: Reading Effectively

1. What is the topic sentence of this passage?

_____

_____

2. What Key Terms are defined in this passage? What are their meanings?

_____

_____

3. Describe the structure of a *grain.*

_____

_____

Circle the letter of the phrase that best answers the question.

4. What percent of the world's cultivated farmland is used for growing crops other than cereal grains?
   a. about 15 percent
   b. about 30 percent
   c. about 50 percent
   d. about 70 percent

Name_____ Date _____ Class_____

CHAPTER
(25) ACTIVE READING

—Plant Reproduction

▶ Section 25-1: Sexual Reproduction in Seedless Plants

Read the passage below, which is reproduced from page 551 of your textbook. Answer the questions that follow.

The life cycle of a fern begins when a diploid sporophyte produces spores by meiosis. The haploid spores fall to the ground
and grow into haploid gametophytes. Fern gametophytes produce gametes by mitosis—eggs in archegonia and sperm in
antheridia. When water covers a gametophyte, sperm can swim
to archegonia and fertilize the eggs inside them. A fertilized
egg, or zygote, grows into a new sporophyte, which destroys the
gametophyte from which it grows.

Read each question and write your answer in the space provided.

SKILL: Reading Effectively

1. What is the function of meiosis in the life cycle of a fern?

_____

2. What is the function of mitosis in the life cycle of a fern?

_____

3. What can occur when water covers a fern gametophyte?

_____

_____

SKILL: Sequencing Information

4. Arrange the five major steps below in the order in which they occur in the
life cycle of a fern. Write a *1* in the space provided for the first step,
write a *2* in the space provided for the second step, and so on.

   a. _____ Gametophytes produce gametes inside antheridia and archegonia.

   b. _____ A mature sporophyte produces spores in clusters of sporangia.

   c. _____ Sperm swim through a film of water and fertilize eggs inside archegonia.

   d. _____ A zygote develops into a new sporophyte.

   e. _____ Spores grow into a heart-shaped gametophyte.

(continued on the next page)

5. The figure below shows the life cycle of a fern. Insert the following labels in the space provided: archegonium, sporangium, spores, adult sporophyte, fertilization, mature gametophyte, mitosis, and zygote. You will use one term more than once.

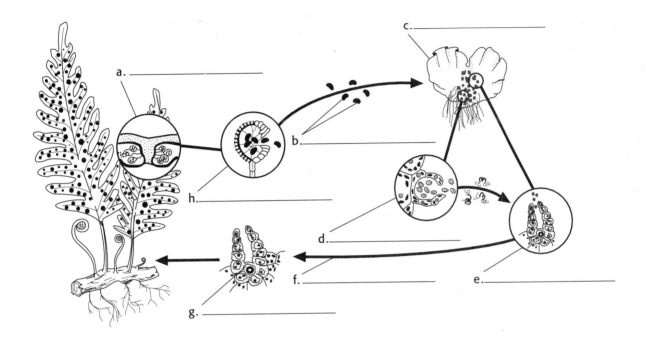

a. _____

c. _____

b. _____

h. _____

d. _____

f. _____

e. _____

g. _____

An analogy is a comparison. Circle the letter of the word that best completes the analogy.

6. Sperm is to antheridia as eggs are to

   a. meiosis.
   b. mitosis.
   c. archegonia.
   d. spores.

CHAPTER
25 ACTIVE READING

Plant Reproduction

▶ **Section 25-2: Sexual Reproduction in Seed Plants**

Read the passage below, which is reproduced from page 556 of your textbook. Answer the questions that follow.

In angiosperms, gametophytes develop within flowers. Flower parts are arranged in four concentric whorls. The outermost whorl consists of one or more **sepals,** which protect the flower from damage while it is a bud. The second whorl consists of one or more **petals,** which attract pollinators. The third whorl consists of one or more **stamens,** which produce pollen. Each stamen is made of a threadlike filament that is topped by a pollen-producing sac called an **anther.** The fourth and innermost whorl of a flower consists of one or more **pistils,** which produce ovules. Ovules develop in a pistil's swollen lower portion, which is called the **ovary.** Usually, a stalk called the style rises from the ovary. Pollen lands on and sticks to the stigma—the swollen, sticky tip of the style.

Read each question and write your answer in the space provided.

SKILL: Reading Effectively

1. How are flower parts arranged?

_____

2. What is the function of *sepals*?

_____

3. What is the function of *petals*?

_____

4. What relationship exists between *stamens* and the *anther*?

_____

An analogy is a comparison. Circle the letter of word that best completes the analogy.

5. Ovules are to pistil as pollen is to
   a. stamens.
   b. sepals.
   c. stigma.
   d. bud.

Name_____ Date_____ Class_____

Plant Reproduction

▶ Section 25-3: Asexual Reproduction

Read the passage below, which is reproduced from page 562 of your textbook. Answer the questions that follow.

Growing new plants from seed or from vegetative parts is **plant propagation.** Plants are often propagated from structures that the plants have produced for the purpose of vegetative reproduction. The table shown below summarizes some of the methods of vegetative plant propagation that are used widely to grow plants.

Method	Description	Examples
Grafting	Small stems from one plant are attached to larger stems or roots of another plant.	Grape vines, hybrid roses, and fruit and nut trees
Taking cuttings	Leaves or pieces of stems or roots are cut from one plant and used to grow new individuals.	African violets, ornamental trees and shrubs, and figs
Tissue culture	Pieces of tissue from one plant are placed on a sterile medium and used to grow new individuals.	Orchids, potatoes, and many houseplants

Read each question and write your answer in the space provided.

SKILL: Reading Effectively

1. What is *plant propagation*?

_____

2. What methods of vegetative *plant propagation* are described in the table?

_____

3. In addition to naming methods of vegetative *plant propagation*, what other information is contained in the table?

_____
_____
_____

4. What occurs during grafting?

_____

_____

5. What types of plants are often produced by taking cuttings?

_____

_____

An analogy is a comparison. Circle the letter of the word or phrase that best completes the analogy.

6. Grafting is to grape vines as tissue culture is to
    a. figs.
    b. potatoes.
    c. fruit trees.
    d. hybrid roses.

CHAPTER
26 **ACTIVE READING**

Plant Structure and Function

▶ Section 26-1: The Vascular Plant Body

Read the passage below, which is reproduced from page 571 of your textbook. Answer the questions that follow.

Dermal tissue covers the outside of a plant's body. In the non-woody part of a plant, dermal tissue forms a "skin" called the **epidermis.** The word *epidermis* comes from the Greek words *epi,* meaning "upon," and *derma,* meaning "skin." The epidermis of most plants is made up of a single layer of flat cells. A waxy cuticle, which prevents water loss, coats the epidermis of the stems and leaves. Often, the cells of the epidermis have hairlike extensions or other structures. Extensions of the epidermal cells on leaves and stems often help to slow water loss. Extensions of the epidermal cells on root tips help to increase water absorption. The dermal tissue on woody stems and roots consists of several layers of dead cells, which are referred to as **cork.** Cork cells contain a waterproof chemical and are not covered by a waxy cuticle. In addition to protection, dermal tissue also helps in gas exchange and in the absorption of mineral nutrients.

Read each question and write your answer in the space provided.

SKILL: Reading Effectively

1. What is the origin of the term *epidermis*?

_____

_____

2. What is the function of the waxy cuticle that covers the *epidermis* of stems and leaves?

_____

_____

3. How is the function of extensions of epidermal cells on leaves and stems different from the function of extensions on root tips?

_____

_____

4. What is *cork*?

_____

_____

5. What are three jobs of dermal tissue?

_____

_____

Circle the letter of the phrase that best completes the statement.

6. The epidermis of most plants is made up of
   a. several layers of dead cells.
   b. a double layer of thick cells.
   c. a single layer of flat cells.
   d. a single layer of dead cells.

CHAPTER
26 ACTIVE READING

Plant Structure and Function

▶ Section 26-2: Transport in Plants

Read the passage below, which is reproduced from page 579 of your textbook. Answer the questions that follow.

A stoma is surrounded by a pair of guard cells that are shaped like two cupped hands. Changes in water pressure within the guard cells cause the stoma to open or close. When the guard cells take in water, they swell. However, extra cellulose strands in their cell walls permit the cells to increase in length but not in diameter. As a result, guard cells that take in water bend away from each other, opening the stoma and allowing transpiration to proceed. When water leaves the guard cells, they shorten and move closer to each other, closing the stoma and stopping transpiration. Thus, the loss of water from guard cells for any reason causes stomata to close, stopping further water loss. This is an example of homeostasis in action.

Read each question and write your answer in the space provided.

SKILL: Recognizing Cause and Effect

1. Events may be linked through a cause-and-effect relationship. The first event to occur, or the cause, triggers a second event, or the effect, to happen. In the spaces below, identify the cause or effect in each relationship.

   a. Cause: _____
   Effect: Guard cells open or close.

   b. Cause: Guard cells take in water.

   Effect: _____

   c. Cause: _____
   Effect: The guard cells increase in length but not in diameter.

   d. Cause: Guard cells that take in water bend away from each other.

   Effect: _____

   e. Cause: _____
   Effect: Guard cells shorten and move closer together.

   f. Cause: The stoma closes.

   Effect: _____

2. The figures below show control of a stomatal opening. In the spaces provided, describe what is occurring in each figure.

Part a.   **Part b.**

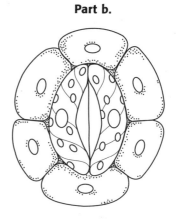

a. Part a. _____

_____

_____

b. Part b. _____

_____

_____

Circle the letter of the word or phrase that best completes the statement.

3. A stoma is surrounded by a pair of guard cells that are shaped like two
   a. rough stems.
   b. cupped hands.
   c. smooth petals.
   d. flat boards.

Name _____ Date _____ Class _____

CHAPTER
27 ACTIVE READING

Plant Growth and Development

▶ Section 27-1: How Plants Grow and Develop

Read the passage below, which is reproduced from page 591 of your textbook. Answer the questions that follow.

Depending on how long it lives, a plant can be classified as one of three basic types: perennial, annual, or biennial. Many herbaceous plants and all woody plants are perennials. A **perennial** is a plant that lives for several years. Most perennials reproduce many times during their life span. Others reproduce only once before they die. Chrysanthemums, daffodils, and irises are familiar herbaceous perennials.

Sunflowers, beans, corn, and many weeds are annuals. An **annual** is a plant that completes its life cycle and then dies within one growing season. Virtually all annuals are herbaceous plants.

Carrots, parsley, and onions are biennials. A **biennial** is a flowering plant that takes two growing seasons to complete its life cycle. During the first season, a biennial produces roots and shoots that store nutrients. In the second season, it uses the stored nutrients to produce a flowering stalk. The plant dies after producing seeds.

Read each question and write your answer in the space provided.

SKILL: Reading Effectively

1. Write *P* on the line if the statement describes perennials, *A* if the statement describes annuals, or *B* if the statement describes biennials.

   a. _____ virtually all are herbaceous plants

   b. _____ live for several years

   c. _____ life cycle spans two growing seasons

   d. _____ most reproduce many times during their life

   e. _____ die within one growing season

Circle the letter of the word or phrase that best completes the statement.

2. All of the following plants are biennials EXCEPT
   a. onions.
   b. carrots.
   c. parsley.
   d. corn.

Plant Growth and Development

▶ Section 27-2: Regulating Plant Growth and Development

Read the passage below, which is reproduced from page 600 of your textbook. Answer the questions that follow.

A **tropism** is a response in which a plant grows either toward or away from a stimulus. Auxin is responsible for producing tropisms. Phototropisms are responses to light. Responses to gravity are gravitropisms. A thigmotropism is a response to touch. If a plant grows toward a stimulus, the response is called a positive tropism. If a plant grows away from the stimulus, the response is called a negative tropism. Thus, a shoot that grows up out of the ground shows both positive phototropism (growing toward the light) and negative gravitropism (growing away from the pull of gravity).

Read each question and write your answer in the space provided.

SKILL: Reading Effectively

1. The prefix *thigmo-* comes from the Greek word meaning "touch." The base word *tropism* comes from the Greek word meaning "change or turn." Using the meaning of these word parts, define the term *thigmotropism:*

_____

2. The prefix *photo-* comes from the Greek word meaning "light." Using the meaning of this prefix, define the term *phototropism:*

_____

3. How are auxins and *tropisms* related?

_____

4. How are a positive and negative *tropism* alike? How are they different?

_____

_____

_____

_____

Circle the letter of the word or phrase that best completes the statement.

5. The coiling of grapevine tendrils around a wire is an example of
   a. positive thigmotropism.　　　　**c.** negative phototropism.
   b. positive gravitropism.　　　　　**d.** Both (a) and (b)

CHAPTER
(28) **ACTIVE READING**

—Introduction to Animals

▶ Section 28-1: Animals—Features and Body Plans

Read the passage below, which is reproduced from page 620 of your textbook. Answer the questions that follow.

To visually represent the relationships among various groups of animals, scientists often use a type of branching diagram called a family tree, or **phylogenetic tree,** which shows how animals are related through evolution. Scientists determine these relationships by comparing several different types of evidence. Clues to animal relationships can be found in the fossil record and by comparing the anatomy and physiology of living animals. Clues are also found by comparing patterns of development in animal embryos. The most direct evidence of evolutionary relationships, however, comes from comparing the DNA in the genes of various animal species.

Read each question and write your answer in the space provided.

SKILL: Reading Effectively

1. What is a *phylogenetic tree*?

_____

_____

2. What are four ways that scientists obtain clues to the evolutionary relationships that exist among animals?

_____

_____

_____

_____

Circle the letter of the word or phrase that best completes the statement.

3. Which phyla possesses members that have a notochord?
   a. Cnidaria   **c.** Platyhelminthes
   b. Annelida   **d.** Chordata

Introduction to Animals

▶ Section: 28-2: Animal Body Systems

Read the passage below, which is reproduced from page 627 of your textbook. Answer the questions that follow.

Reproduction that does not involve the fusion of two gametes is called asexual reproduction. A sponge, for example, can reproduce by simply fragmenting its body. Each fragment grows into a new sponge. An unusual method of asexual reproduction is **parthenogenesis,** in which a new individual develops from an unfertilized egg.

In sexual reproduction, a new individual is formed by the union of a male gamete and a female gamete. Gametes are produced in the gonads, or sex organs. The testes produce the male gametes (sperm), and the ovaries produce the female gametes (eggs). Some species of animals, called hermaphrodites, have both testes and ovaries. Many simple invertebrates, including slugs, earthworms, and some fishes, are hermaphrodites.

Read each question and write your answer in the space provided.

SKILL: Reading Effectively

1. Complete each statement by writing the correct letter in the space provided. Write *A* if the statement is true of asexual reproduction, write *S* if the statement is true of sexual reproduction, write *B* if the statement is true of both forms of reproduction.

a. _____ necessary for a species to survive

b. _____ dependent on the actions of the testes and ovaries

c. _____ one form is parthenogenesis

d. _____ occurs in animals

e. _____ unites male and female gametes

f. _____ a sponge does this by body fragmentation

An analogy is a comparison. Circle the letter of the word or phrase that best completes the analogy.

2. Sperm is to gametes as testes are to
   a. ovaries.   c. hermaphrodites.
   b. gonads.   d. eggs.

CHAPTER

(29) ACTIVE READING

Simple Invertebrates

▶ Section 29-1: Sponges

Read the passage below, which is reproduced from page 639 of your textbook. Notice that the sentences are numbered. Answer the questions that follow.

[1] Sponges frequently reproduce by simply breaking off fragments, each of which develops into a new individual. [2] Sponges also reproduce by budding. [3] Another form of asexual reproduction occurs in some freshwater sponges. [4] When living conditions become harsh (cold or very dry), some freshwater sponges ensure their survival by forming **gemmules,** clusters of amoebocytes encased in protective coats. [5] Sealed in with ample food, the cells survive even if the rest of the sponge dies. [6] When conditions improve, the cells grow into a new sponge.

Read each question and write your answer in the space provided.

1. What Key Term is defined in this passage? What does this term mean?

_____

_____

2. What is the main idea of this passage?

_____

_____

SKILL: Recognizing Cause and Effect

3. A cause-and-effect relationship identifies how events are linked. The first event to occur, or the cause, triggers a second event, or effect, to happen. Identify the cause-and-effect of the relationship identified in Sentence 1.

_____

_____

_____

4. Identify the cause-and-effect of the relationship described in Sentence 4.

_____

_____

_____

5. Identify the cause-and-effect of the relationship described in Sentence 5.

_____

_____

6. Identify the cause-and-effect of the relationship described in Sentence 6.

_____

_____

Circle the letter of the word or phrase that best answers the question.

7. What does the term *ample* mean in Sentence 5?
   a. sufficient
   b. plentiful
   c. vast
   d. meager

CHAPTER
(29) **ACTIVE READING**

Simple Invertebrates

▶ Section 29-2: Cnidarians

Read the passage below, which is reproduced from page 640 of your textbook. Answer the questions that follow.

Cnidarians have two basic body forms, both of which show radial symmetry. **Medusa** forms are free-floating, jellylike, and often umbrella-shaped. **Polyp** forms are tubelike and are usually attached to a rock or some other object. A fringe of tentacles surround the mouth, located at the free end of the body. Many cnidarians exist only as medusas, while others exist only as polyps. Still others alternate between these two phases during the course of their life cycle.

The cnidarian body has two layers of cells, the outer is ectoderm and the inner layer is endoderm.

Read each question and write your answer in the space provided.

SKILL: Interpreting Graphics

1. The figures below show the two body forms of cnidarians. Using the information contained in the passage, classify each form as either medusa or polyp. Then, in the spaces provided, label the following parts of each form: mouth, tentacle, ectoderm, and endoderm.

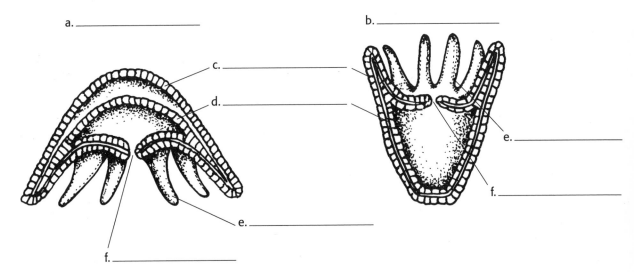

a. _____   b. _____

c. _____

d. _____

e. _____   e. _____

f. _____   f. _____

Circle the letter of the word or phrase that best completes the statement.

2. All cnidarians have a body form that
   a. resembles an umbrella.
   b. has three layers of cells.
   c. shows radial symmetry.
   d. changes during the life of the organism.

CHAPTER

29 **ACTIVE READING**

—Simple Invertebrates

▶ **Section 29-3: Flatworms and Roundworms**

Read the passage below, which is reproduced from page 651 of your textbook. Answer the questions that follow.

Roundworms have long, cylindrical bodies and are the simplest animals to have a one-way digestive system. A flexible, thick layer of epidermis and cuticle form a protective cover and give the roundworm's body its shape. Beneath this cover, a layer of muscle extends along the length of the worm. These long muscles pull against the cuticle and the pseudocoelom (false body cavity), whipping the worm's body from side to side. While some roundworms grow to be 1 ft or more in length, most are microscopic or only a few millimeters long. The vast majority of roundworms are free-living, active hunters.

Read each question and write your answer in the space provided.

SKILL: Reading Effectively

1. What is the function of the thick layer of epidermis and cuticle that covers the roundworm's body?

_____

_____

2. What parts of the human body share this function?

_____

_____

3. Based on the last two sentences of the passage, what are three traits shared by most roundworms?

_____

_____

Circle the letter of the word or phrase that best completes the statement.

4. Roundworms are the simplest animals to have a
   a. simple circulatory system.   **c.** complex respiratory system.
   b. one-way digestive system.   **d.** Both (a) and (b)

CHAPTER
30 **ACTIVE READING**

Mollusks and Annelids

▶ Section 30-1: Mollusks

Read the passage below, which is reproduced from page 661 of your textbook. Answer the questions that follow.

Despite their varied appearance, the members of the different groups of mollusks share a number of key characteristics.

The body of every mollusk has three distinct parts: the visceral mass, the mantle, and the muscular foot. The **visceral mass** is a central section that contains the mollusk's organs. Wrapped around the visceral mass like a cape is a heavy fold of tissues called the **mantle,** which forms the outer layer of the body. Finally, every mollusk has a muscular region called a **foot,** which is used primarily for locomotion.

Read each question and write your answer in the space provided.

SKILL: Interpreting Graphics

1. The figure below shows the body of a mollusk. In the spaces provided, label the following parts of the mollusk: foot, mantle, mantle cavity, and visceral mass.

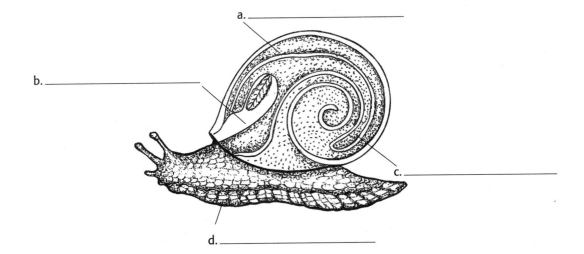

(continued on next page)

Read each question and write your answer in the space provided.

SKILL: Reading Effectively

2. Which part is used for locomotion?

_____

_____

3. Which part contains the mollusk's organs?

_____

_____

4. Which part forms the outer layer of the organism?

_____

_____

An analogy is a comparison. Circle the letter of the word or phrase that best completes the analogy.

5. Mollusk is to mantle as human is to
   a. skin.
   b. arm.
   c. heart.
   d. brain.

— Mollusks and Annelids

▶ Section 30-2: Annelids

Read the passage below, which is reproduced from page 669 of your textbook. Answer the questions that follow.

Annelids are easily recognized by their external segments, which are visible as a series of ringlike structures along the length of their body. Each segment contains digestive, excretory, and locomotor (movement) organs. Some of the segments are modified for specific functions, such as reproduction, feeding, or sensation. A well-developed **cerebral ganglion,** or primitive brain, is located in one anterior segment.

Internal body walls, called **septa,** separate the segments of most annelids. Nutrients and other materials pass between the segments through the circulatory system, while sensory information is delivered by a nerve cord that connects nerve centers in the segments to the brain.

Read each question and write your answer in the space provided.

SKILL: Reading Effectively

1. What organ types are found in each segment of an annelid's body?

   _____

   _____

2. Why does the word *movement* appear in parentheses?

   _____

   _____

3. What are some functions for which a particular segment is modified?

   _____

   _____

An analogy is a comparison. Circle the letter of the word or phrase that best completes the analogy.

4. Bivalve is to shells as annelid is to
   a. foot.   **c.** gills.
   b. segments.   **d.** brain.

CHAPTER
31 **ACTIVE READING**

—Arthropods

▶ Section 31-1: Features of Arthropods

Read the passage below, which is reproduced from page 686 of your textbook. Answer the questions that follow.

A tough exoskeleton protects an arthropod from predators and helps prevent water loss. But an exoskeleton cannot grow larger, so an arthropod cannot simply grow bigger, as many other animals do. Imagine blowing up a balloon inside a soft drink can—after a certain point, the balloon cannot get any bigger. Arthropods have the same problem, so they need to shed and discard their exoskeletons periodically in a process called **molting,** or ecdysis. Molting is triggered by the release of certain hormones. Just before molting, a new exoskeleton forms beneath the old one. When the new exoskeleton is fully formed, the old one breaks open. The arthropod emerges in its new, still-soft exoskeleton. The new exoskeleton hardens within a few hours or a few days, depending on the species.

Read each question and write your answer in the space provided.

SKILL: Reading Effectively

1. The prefix *exo-* means "outside of." Using this prefix, define the term *exoskeleton.*

_____

_____

2. What are two functions of an arthropod's exoskeleton?

_____

_____

3. What is a synonym for *molting*?

_____

_____

Circle the letter of the word or phrase that best completes the statement.

4. Molting is triggered by the release of certain
   a. bones.   **c.** air valves.
   b. hormones.   **d.** blood cells.

CHAPTER
31 **ACTIVE READING**

— Arthropods

▶ Section 31-2: Spiders and Other Arachnids

Read the passage below, which is reproduced from page 688 of your textbook. Answer the questions that follow.

The arachnid body is made up of a cephalothorax and an abdomen. There are no antennae, and the first pair of appendages are chelicerae. The second pair of appendages are **pedipalps,** which are modified to catch and handle prey. (The pedipalps are sometimes specialized for sensory or even reproductive functions.) Following the pedipalps are four pairs of appendages called walking legs.

All arachnids except mites are carnivores, and most are terrestrial. Since arachnids do not have jaws, they are able to consume only liquid food. To do so, the arachnid first injects its prey with powerful enzymes that cause the prey's tissues to liquefy. Then the arachnid sucks the liquid food into its stomach.

Read each question and write your answer in the space provided.

SKILL: Reading Effectively

1. Describe the two main parts of an arachnid body.

_____

_____

2. How many pairs of appendages does an arachnid have? Describe these appendages.

_____

_____

_____

3. What are the functions of *pedipalps*?

_____

_____

Circle the letter of the word or phrase that best completes the statement.

4. The arachnid body lacks
   a. antennae. **c.** walking legs.
   b. jaws. **d.** Both (a) and (b)

CHAPTER
31 **ACTIVE READING**

Arthropods

▶ Section 31-3: Insects and Their Relatives

Read the passage below, which is reproduced from page 693 of your textbook. Answer the questions that follow.

The life cycles of most insects are complex, and often several molts are required before the adult stage is reached. During the last molt, the young insect undergoes a dramatic physical change called **metamorphosis.**

Complete metamorphosis: Almost all insect species undergo complete metamorphosis. In complete metamorphosis, the wingless, wormlike larva encloses itself within a protective capsule called a **chrysalis.** Here it passes through a **pupa** stage, in which it changes into an adult.

Although a complete metamorphosis might seem unnecessarily complex, the larvae exploit different habitats and food sources than adults do. This ecological separation of young from adults eliminates competition, thus increasing the chance of survival for each phase of the life cycle.

Incomplete metamorphosis: A smaller number of species develops into adults in a much less dramatic incomplete metamorphosis. In these species, the egg hatches into a juvenile, or **nymph,** that looks like a small, wingless adult. After several molts, the nymph develops into an adult.

Read each question and write your answer in the space provided.

SKILL: Recognizing Similarities and Differences

1. Write *C* on the line if the phrase describes a complete metamorphosis. Write *I* on the line if the phrase describes an incomplete metamorphosis. Write *B* on the line if the phrase applies to both types of metamorphosis.

   a. _____ larva encloses itself in a chrysalis

   b. _____ product is an adult

   c. _____ egg hatches into a nymph

   d. _____ involves several molts

   e. _____ involves a pupa stage

   f. _____ begins with an egg

g. _____ nymph goes through several molts

h. _____ food sources of larvae are different from those of adults

i. _____ majority of insects undergo this series of physical changes

j. _____ larva never enters a protective capsule

Circle the letter of the word or phrase that best completes the statement.

2. The ecological separation of young from adults during complete metamorphosis eliminates
   a. the need to care for young.
   b. competition.
   c. adaptation.
   d. Both (a) and (b)

—Arthropods

▶ Section 31-4: Crustaceans

Read the passage below, which is reproduced from page 698 of your textbook. Answer the questions that follow.

Just as insect species dominate on land, crustaceans abound in the world's oceans. Their great numbers have earned them the nickname "the insects of the sea." Many are microscopic creatures that drift as plankton in the ocean currents. While primarily marine, members of the subphylum Crustacea are also found in fresh water and in a few terrestrial habitats. Crustaceans include crabs, lobsters, crayfish, shrimps, barnacles, water fleas, and pill bugs.

Almost all crustaceans have a distinctive larval form called a **nauplius.** The nauplius has three pairs of branched appendages. Like insects, the nauplius undergoes a series of molts before it takes on its adult form.

Adult crustaceans also have mandibles as insects do, but crustaceans differ from insects in a number of important respects.

Crustaceans have two pairs of antennae, while insects have one pair. While both crustaceans and insects have walking legs, these appendages are attached to the thorax and abdomen of a crustacean but are attached only to the thorax of an insect. In addition, a crustacean takes in oxygen through gills, while an insect takes in oxygen through its tracheal system.

Read each question and write your answer in the space provided.

SKILL: Reading Effectively

1. Why are crustaceans called "the insects of the sea"?

_____

_____

_____

2. What are two possible crustacean habitats?

_____

_____

_____

3. What is a nauplius? What does a nauplius undergo before taking adult form?

_____

_____

_____

SKILL: Recognizing Similarities and Differences

4. Complete the chart to compare characteristics of crustaceans and insects.

Crustaceans	Insects
a.	b.
c.	d.
e.	f.

Circle the letter of the word or phrase that best completes the statement.

5. All of the following are types of crustaceans EXCEPT
    a. chrysalis.
    b. barnacles.
    c. crayfish.
    d. pill bugs.

CHAPTER
(32) **ACTIVE READING**

Echinoderms and Invertebrate Chordates

► Section 32-1: Echinoderms

Read the passage below, which is reproduced from page 710 of your textbook. Answer the questions that follow.

During its development, an embryo goes through a gastrula stage. A gastrula has an opening to the outside called the **blastopore.** In acoelomate animals, the mouth develops from or near the blastopore. This pattern of development also occurs in some coelomate animals, such as annelids, mollusks, and arthropods. Animals with mouths that develop from or near the blastopore are called **protostomes.**

Some animals follow a different pattern of development. In phylums Echinodermata and Chordata, the anus—not the mouth—develops from or near the blastopore. (The mouth forms later, on another part of the embryo.) Animals with this pattern of development are called **deuterostomes.** If you know the origin of the terms *protostomes* and *deuterostomes*, it's easy to remember the difference between the two developmental patterns. The term *protostome* is from the Greek *protos*, meaning "first," and *stoma*, meaning "mouth." The prefix *deutero-* is from the Greek *deuteros*, meaning "second." In deuterostomes, the anus develops first and the mouth develops second.

Read each question and write your answer in the space provided.

SKILL: Reading Effectively

1. What is the meaning of the Key Term *blastopore*?

_____

_____

2. What develops from or near the *blastopore* in acoelomate animals?

_____

_____

3. What two phylums have a different pattern of development?

_____

_____

4. How would knowledge of the word parts *protos* and *stoma* help you define the word *protostomes*?

_____

_____

_____

_____

_____

5. How would knowledge of the word parts *deutero* and *stoma* help you define the word *deuterostomes*?

_____

_____

_____

_____

_____

SKILL: Interpreting Graphics

6. The figure illustrates two patterns of embryonic development for a gastrula. Label a. or b. as protostome or deuterostome. Label the following parts of the figure: blastopore, coelom, and gut. You will use the labels more than once.

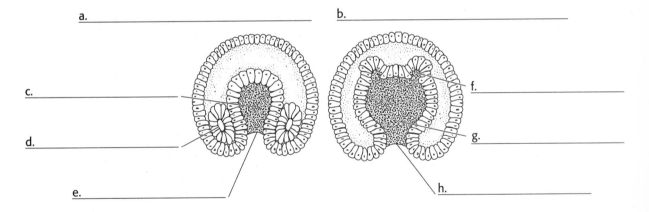

a. _____ b. _____

c. _____

d. _____

e. _____

f. _____

g. _____

h. _____

Circle the letter of the word or phrase that best completes the statement.

7. Protostomes and deuterostomes are alike in that both groups of animals have

   a. a blastopore in their gastrula stage.
   b. an anus that develops from the gut.
   c. a coelom in their gastrula stage.
   d. Both (a) and (b)

CHAPTER
32 **ACTIVE READING**

Echinoderms and Invertebrate Chordates

► Section 32-2: Invertebrate Chordates

Read the passage below, which is reproduced from page 718 of your textbook. Answer the questions that follow.

The second major group of deuterostomes are the **chordates.** Chordates have a very different kind of endoskeleton, one that is completely internal. During the development of the chordate embryo, a stiff rod called the **notochord** develops along the back of the embryo. The evolution of an internal skeleton was an important step that led to the evolution of vertebrates. The endoskeleton, which muscles attach to, made it possible for animals to grow large and move quickly.

Chordates also share three other characteristics. They have a single, hollow, dorsal nerve cord with nerves attached to it that travel to different parts of the body. Chordates also have a series of **pharyngeal slits** (openings) that develop in the wall of the pharynx, the muscular tube that connects the mouth to the digestive tract and the windpipe. Another chordate characteristic is a postanal tail, which is a tail that extends beyond the anus. All chordates have all four of these characteristics at some time in their life, even if it is only briefly as embryos.

Read each question and write your answer in the space provided.

SKILL: Reading Effectively

1. The prefix *endo-* means "inside or within." Using the meaning of this prefix, define the word *endoskeleton*.

_____

_____

2. What capabilities were made possible for animals due to the evolution of an internal skeleton?

_____

_____

3. Where do the series of pharyngeal slits develop in chordates?

_____

_____

4. Where does the *notochord* develop in *chordates*?

_____

_____

Circle the letter of the word or phrase that best completes the statement.

5. The evolution of an internal skeleton was an important step that led to the evolution of

    a. vertebrates.
    b. deuterostomes.
    c. invertebrates.
    d. amoebas.

Introduction to Vertebrates

▶ Section 33-1: Vertebrates Spread from the Sea to the Land

Read the passage below, which is reproduced from page 730 of your textbook. Answer the questions that follow.

Vertebrates are chordates with a backbone. They take their name from the individual segments, called **vertebrae,** that make up the backbone. In most vertebrates, the backbone completely replaces the notochord found in invertebrate chordates.

The backbone provides support for and protects a dorsal nerve cord. It also provides a site for muscle attachment. These functions paved the way for the development of an internal skeleton that allowed vertebrates to grow larger than their invertebrate ancestors. In addition to a backbone, most vertebrates have a bony skull that encases and protects their brain.

Vertebrates share a number of other characteristics, including segmentation, bilateral symmetry, and two pairs of jointed appendages, such as limbs or fins. They exhibit cephalization and have a complex brain and sense organs. All vertebrates have a true coelom and a closed circulatory system with a chambered heart.

Read each question and write your answer in the space provided.

SKILL: Reading Effectively

1. What are three functions of the backbone?

_____

_____

_____

_____

An analogy is a comparison. Circle the letter of the word or phrase that best completes the analogy.

2. Vertebrate is to backbone as invertebrate is to
   a. brain.   **c.** circulatory system.
   b. sense organs.   **d.** notochord.

CHAPTER
(33) ACTIVE READING

Introduction to Vertebrates

▶ Section 33-2: Vertebrates Adapt to Terrestrial Living

Read the passage below, which is reproduced from page 742 of your textbook. Answer the questions that follow.

Ectothermic animals, such as today's living reptiles, have a metabolism too slow to produce enough heat to warm their body. Such animals must absorb heat from their environment, and their body temperature changes as the temperature of the environment changes. Ectotherms are sometimes referred to as cold-blooded. Other vertebrates, such as mammals and birds, are **endothermic,** that is, they maintain a high, constant body temperature by producing heat internally through a faster metabolism. Endotherms are sometimes called warmblooded.

Read each question and write your answer in the space provided.

SKILL: Reading Effectively

1. The prefix *endo-* means "inside or within," while the prefix *ecto-* means "outside or external." The term *therm* means "heat." How does knowledge of these word parts aid in defining the two Key Terms contained in this passage?

_____

_____

2. Why must reptiles absorb heat from their environment?

_____

_____

3. Why are birds able to maintain a constant body temperature?

_____

_____

An analogy is a comparison. Circle the letter of the word or phrase that best completes the analogy.

4. Cold-blooded is to reptile as warm-blooded is to
   a. mammals.
   b. insects.
   c. plants.
   d. Both (a) and (b)

Fishes and Amphibians

▶ Section 34-1: The Fish Body

Read the passage below, which is reproduced from page 757 of your textbook. Answer the questions that follow.

The major respiratory organ of a fish is the gill. Each gill is made up of two rows of **gill filaments** which hang like curtains between a fish's mouth and cheeks. At the rear of the cheek cavity is an opening called a **gill slit**. As a fish swallows water it forces the water from the mouth, over the gills, and out through the gill slits. This swallowing procedure, one-way water flow through the gills combined with a specific arrangement of gill tissue, permits countercurrent water flow. In **countercurrent flow,** the water passing across the gills and the blood circulating in the capillary networks through the gills flow in opposite directions. Countercurrent flow ensures that oxygen diffuses into the blood over the entire length of the capillaries in the gills. Due to this arrangement, the gills of bony fishes are able to extract up to 85 percent of the oxygen in the water passing over them.

Read each question and write your answer in the space provided.

SKILL: Reading Effectively

1. Why does a fish "swallow" water?

_____

_____

2. How are gills and *gill slits* related?

_____

_____

3. How does *countercurrent flow* increase the efficiency of a bony fish's gills?

_____

_____

Circle the letter of the word or phrase that best completes the statement.

4. The major respiratory organ of a bony fish is the
   a. lung.   **c.** gill.
   b. gill filament. **d.** Both (a) and (b)

Fishes and Amphibians

▶ Section 34-2: Today's Fishes

Read the passage below, which is reproduced from page 763 of your textbook. Answer the questions that follow.

In addition to their strong, internal skeleton made completely of bone, bony fishes have a series of unique structural adaptations that contribute greatly to their success.

Lateral line system: Although found in sharks to a limited degree, only bony fishes have a fully developed lateral line system. The **lateral line** is a specialized sensory system that extends along each side of a bony fish's body. As moving water presses against the lateral line, nerve impulses from ciliated sensory cells within it permit the fish to perceive its position and rate of movement. The lateral line system enables a fish to detect a motionless object by the movement of water deflected off that object.

Gill cover: Most bony fishes have a hard plate called an **operculum** that covers the gills on each side of the head. Movement of certain muscles and the opercula permits a bony fish to draw water over the gills, enabling the fish to breathe. By using this mechanism, most bony fishes can move water over their gills while remaining stationary in water. In other words, a bony fish doesn't have to swim forward with its mouth open to move water over its gills. This ability to respire without swimming enables a bony fish to conserve energy that can be spent chasing after prey and escaping from predators.

Swim bladder: Bony fishes contain a special gas sac called a **swim bladder.** By adjusting the gas content of the swim bladder, bony fishes can regulate their buoyancy. The effect is that as the bladder fills, the fish rises, and as the bladder empties, the fish sinks. The swim bladder of early fishes was connected to the throat, and they could gulp air to fill it. The swim bladder of modern bony fishes does not have a direct passage to the mouth. Instead, gas is released from or absorbed into their bloodstream to fill or empty the bladder.

(continued on next page)

Read each question and write your answer in the space provided.

SKILL: Reading Effectively

1. What three structural adaptations are found in bony fishes?

_____

_____

2. What is the *operculum*?

_____

_____

3. How does the ability to respire while stationary aid a bony fish?

_____

_____

_____

4. What is the *lateral line*?

_____

_____

5. What two abilities does a bony fish have due to its *lateral line system*?

_____

_____

6. What is a *swim bladder*?

_____

_____

7. How did early bony fishes fill their *swim bladder*?

_____

_____

_____

Circle the letter of the word or phrase that best completes the statement.

8. As the swim bladder of a bony fish empties, the fish
   a. rises.
   b. moves more rapidly.
   c. sinks.
   d. moves more slowly.

CHAPTER
34 **ACTIVE READING**

Fishes and Amphibians

▶ Section 34-3: Amphibians

Read the passage below, which is reproduced from page 768 of your textbook. Answer the questions that follow.

Most amphibians share these five key characteristics.

Legs: The evolution of legs was an important adaptation for living on land. Frogs, toads, salamanders, and newts have four legs. Caecilians lost their legs during the evolutionary course of adapting to a burrowing existence.

Lungs: Although larval amphibians have gills, most adult amphibians breathe with a pair of lungs (lungless salamanders are an exception).

Double loop circulation: Two large veins called pulmonary veins return oxygen-rich blood from the lungs to the heart. Oxygen-rich blood is then pumped to the body tissues at a much higher pressure than when it leaves the lungs.

Partially divided heart: The atrium of the amphibian heart is divided into left and right sides, but the ventricle is not. A mixture of oxygen-rich and oxygen-poor blood is delivered to the amphibian's body tissues.

Cutaneous respiration: Most amphibians supplement their oxygen intake by respiring directly through their moist skin. Cutaneous breathing (skin breathing) limits the maximum body size of amphibians because it is efficient only when there is a high ratio of skin surface area to body volume.

Read each question and write your answer in the space provided.

SKILL: Reading Effectively

1. Why do caecilians lack legs?

_____

_____

_____

_____

2. How is blood delivered to an amphibian's body tissues?

_____

_____

3. What is cutaneous respiration?

_____

_____

4. How does cutaneous respiration limit the body size of an amphibian?

_____

_____

_____

Circle the letter of the word or phrase that best completes the statement.

5. All of the following amphibians have four legs EXCEPT
   a. lungless salamanders.
   b. newts.
   c. toads.
   d. caecilians.

Reptiles and Birds

▶ Section 35-1: The Reptilian Body

Read the passage below, which is reproduced from page 783 of your textbook. Answer the questions that follow.

Reptiles' ectothermic metabolism is too slow to generate enough heat to warm their body, so reptiles must absorb heat from their surroundings. As a result, a reptile's body temperature is largely determined by the temperature of its environment. Many reptiles regulate their temperature behaviorally, by basking in the sun to warm up or seeking shade to cool down. A lizard can maintain a relatively constant body temperature throughout the day by moving between sunlight and shade. At very cold temperatures, most reptiles become sluggish and unable to function. Intolerance of cold generally limits their geographical range and, in cooler climates, forces them to hibernate through winter.

Read each question and write your answer in the space provided.

SKILL: Recognizing Cause and Effect

1. Two independent events can be linked through a cause-and-effect relationship. The first event to occur, or cause, triggers a second event, or effect, to happen. Identify the missing part of each cause-and-effect relationship described below.

   a. Cause: A reptile's ectothermic metabolism is too slow to generate enough heat to warm its body.

   Effect:_____

   _____

   b. Cause: A reptile basks in the sun.

   Effect:_____

   _____

   c. Cause: A lizard spends part of its day in sunlight and part in shade.

   Effect:_____

Circle the letter of the word or phrase that best completes the statement.

2. Most reptiles deal with the cold winters of a cooler climate by

   a. hibernating.   **c.** changing their metabolism.
   b. migrating.   **d.** Both (a) and (b)

Reptiles and Birds

▶ Section 35-2: Today's Reptiles

Read the passage below, which is reproduced from page 792 of your textbook. Answer the questions that follow.

Turtles and tortoises differ from other reptiles in that their bodies are encased within a hard, bony, protective shell. Many of them can pull their head and legs into the shell for effective protection from predators. While most tortoises have a dome-shaped shell, water-dwelling turtles have a streamlined, disk-shaped shell that permits rapid maneuvering in water. Turtles and tortoises lack teeth but have jaws covered by sharp plates. Many are herbivores, but some, such as the snapping turtle, are aggressive carnivores.

Today's turtles and tortoises differ little from the earliest known turtle fossils, which are more than 200 million years old. This evolutionary stability may reflect the continuing benefit of their basic shell-covered body design.

Read each question and write your answer in the space provided.

SKILL: Reading Effectively

1. How are turtles and tortoises different from other reptiles?

_____

_____

_____

2. Are all shells alike? Give examples.

_____

_____

_____

Circle the letter of the word or phrase that best completes the statement.

3. Snapping turtles differ from most other turtles and tortoises in that snapping turtles
   a. are herbivores.
   b. have a unique shell design.
   c. are water-dwellers.
   d. are carnivores.

Reptiles and Birds

▶ Section 35-3: Characteristics and Diversity of Birds

Read the passage below, which is reproduced from page 796 of your textbook. Answer the questions that follow.

When birds fly, they use a considerable amount of energy. Since birds often fly for long periods of time, their cellular demand for energy exceeds that of even the most active mammal.

Reptiles meet their increased need for oxygen with lungs that have a larger surface area than the lungs of amphibians. But there is a limit to how much the efficiency of a lung can be improved by just increasing its surface area. Another way to increase the efficiency of a lung is to modify it so that air passes over its respiratory surface in one direction only, just as water flows over a fish's gills in one direction. This is what happened in birds. One-way air flow was made possible by the evolution of a series of air sacs connected to the bird's lungs.

There are two important advantages to one-way air flow. First, the lungs are exposed only to almost fully oxygenated air, increasing the amount of oxygen transported to the body cells. Second, the flow of blood in the lungs runs in a different direction than the flow of air. While the flow of air and blood are not completely opposite, as in fish gills, the difference in direction does increase oxygen absorption.

Read each question and write your answer in the space provided.

SKILL: Reading Effectively

1. What are the advantages of one-way air flow?

_____

_____

_____

_____

Circle the letter of the word or phrase that best completes the statement.

2. In both birds and fish, air and blood flow in
   a. completely opposite directions.   **c.** different directions.
   b. the same direction.   **d.** parallel paths.

CHAPTER
36 ACTIVE READING

Mammals

▶ Section 36-1: The Mammalian Body

Read the passage below, which is reproduced from page 810 of your textbook. Answer the questions that follow.

Of all animal species only the mammals have hair. Even whales and dolphins, both of which appear to be hairless, have a few sensitive bristles on their snout. A **hair** is a filament composed mainly of dead cells filled with the protein keratin. The evolutionary origin of hair is unknown, but it probably is not derived from reptilian scales.

The primary function of hair is insulation. Mammals, such as the polar bear, typically maintain body temperatures higher than the temperature of their surroundings. As a result, they tend to lose body heat. To reduce the loss of body heat to the environment, most mammals are covered with a dense coat of hair that holds heat in.

Hair has functions other than insulation. The coloration and pattern of a mammal's coat often enable it to blend in with its surroundings. Some animals show a seasonal change in the color of their coat that provides protective coloration year round. The color of a mammal's coat may also be a clear warning signal; the black and white fur of a skunk cautions would-be predators to stay away.

In some animals, special hairs serve a sensory function. Mammals that are active at night or that live underground often rely on their whiskers for information about the environment. Other special hairs, such as a porcupine's sharp quills, can be used as a defensive weapon.

Read each question and write your answer in the space provided.

SKILL: Reading Effectively

1. What is *hair* composed of? Which species have hair?

_____

_____

_____

_____

2. According to the passage, what is the primary function of *hair*?

_____

_____

3. Why do mammals tend to lose body heat?

_____

_____

_____

_____

4. What other functions does *hair* serve?

_____

_____

Circle the letter of the word or phrase that best completes the statement.

5. Whiskers help certain mammals
   a. maintain a particular body temperature.
   b. gather information about the environment.
   c. defend themselves against predators.
   d. Both (a) and (b)

CHAPTER
36 **ACTIVE READING**

—Mammals

▶ Section 36-2: Today's Mammals

Read the passage below, which is reproduced from page 819 of your textbook. Answer the questions that follow.

Order Marsupialia includes not just kangaroos but opossums, wombats, wallaroos, and the koalas. Today, almost all marsupial species are found in the Australian region—Australia, New Guinea, and a few nearby islands—where the vast majority of mammalian species are marsupials. This limited distribution is the result of the breakup of Pangaea. About 70 million years ago, the Australian region became separated from the continents of Antarctica and South America. As placental mammals had not yet reached the Australian region, the marsupials there developed in isolation.

Read each question and write your answer in the space provided.

SKILL: Reading Effectively

1. What five organisms belong to Order Marsupialia?

   _____

   _____

2. Suppose you wanted to conduct a study of marsupials in their natural environment. Where would you likely set up your study? Explain why.

   _____

   _____

   _____

   _____

   _____

   _____

   _____

   _____

   _____

3. What caused today's limited distribution of marsupials?

_____

_____

_____

_____

Circle the letter of the word or phrase that best completes the statement.

4. When Pangaea broke up, the Australian region separated from

   a. South America.
   b. Antarctica.
   c. North America.
   d. Both (a) and (b)

Animal Behavior

▶ Section 37-1: Evolution of Behavior

Read the passage below, which is reproduced from page 836 of your textbook. Answer the questions that follow.

Biologists have learned that many kinds of animal behaviors are influenced by genes. Genetically-programmed behavior is often called **innate behavior,** or instinct. The orb spider builds her web exactly the same way every time. There is little or no variation in what she does, and her female offspring will build their webs in exactly the same manner without being taught. This type of innate behavior is called **fixed action pattern behavior** because the action always occurs in the same way.

The development of behaviors through experience is called **learning.** In many animals, learning is very important in determining the final nature of innate behavior. One simple kind of learning is habituation. In habituation, an animal learns to ignore a frequent, harmless stimulus. For example, birds may at first stay away from a garden that has a new scarecrow. But if the position of the scarecrow is not changed on a regular basis, the birds learn to ignore it and go into the garden unafraid.

Read each question and write your answer in the space provided.

SKILL: Reading Effectively

1. According to the passage, what are two factors that influence animal behaviors?

_____

_____

2. What is *innate behavior?*

_____

_____

3. Why is the building of a web by the orb spider called a *fixed action pattern behavior?*

_____

_____

4. What relationship exists between *learning* and *innate behavior*?

_____

_____

_____

_____

5. What is habituation?

_____

_____

_____

_____

Circle the letter of the word or phrase that best answers the question.

6. Based on the passage above, what recommendation would you make to a farmer who puts up a scarecrow to keep birds out of a garden?

   a. Make sure the scarecrow is securely fastened to prevent any movement.
   b. Spray the scarecrow with an offensive odor that is easily detected by birds.
   c. Try to create a scarecrow that can move in the wind.
   d. Both (a) and (b)

Name _____ Date _____ Class _____

Animal Behavior

▶ Section 37-2: Types of Behavior

Read the passage below, which is reproduced from page 843 of your textbook. Answer the questions that follow.

Among animals, vocal communication is most developed in primates. Many primates have a "vocabulary" of sounds that allows them to communicate the identity of specific predators, such as eagles, leopards, and snakes. Primates cannot talk because they are physically unable to produce the sound of speech. But chimpanzees and gorillas can learn to recognize and use a large number of symbols to communicate abstract concepts. Some researchers believe that chimpanzees can combine symbols that they have learned in meaningful ways. However, chimpanzees cannot rearrange symbols to form a new sentence with a different meaning. That requires a very complex brain structure, one found only in humans.

Read each question and write your answer in the space provided.

SKILL: Reading Effectively

1. What type of information can many primates communicate?

_____

_____

_____

_____

2. What prevents primates from using actual speech?

_____

_____

Circle the letter of the word or phrase that best completes the statement.

3. Some researchers believe that chimpanzees can
   a. use symbols to form new sentences.
   b. combine symbols in meaningful ways.
   c. produce speech.
   d. Both (a) and (b)

CHAPTER
38 ACTIVE READING

Introduction to Body Structure

▶ Section 38-1: Body Organization

Read the passage below, which is reproduced from page 856 of your textbook. Answer the questions that follow.

Epithelial tissue: Epithelial tissue lines most body surfaces, and it protects other tissues from dehydration and physical damage. An epithelial layer is usually no more than a few cells thick. The cells are typically flat and thin and have only a small amount of cytoplasm. Epithelial tissue is constantly being replaced as cells die.

Nervous tissue: The nervous system is made of **nervous tissue.** Nervous tissue consists of nerve cells and their supporting cells. Nerve cells carry information about various stimuli throughout the body.

Connective tissue: Various types of **connective tissue** support, protect, and insulate the body. Connective tissue includes fat, cartilage, bone, tendons, and blood. Some connective tissue cells, such as those in bone, are densely packed. Others, such as those found in blood, are farther apart from each other.

Muscle tissue: Three kinds of **muscle tissue** enable the movement of body structures by muscle contractions. The three kinds of muscle tissues are skeletal muscle, smooth muscle, and cardiac muscle.

1. **Skeletal muscle** is considered voluntary muscle because you can control its contractions. Skeletal muscle move bones in the trunk and limbs.

2. **Smooth muscle** is called involuntary muscle because you cannot consciously control its slow, long-lasting contractions. Some smooth muscles, such as those lining the walls of blood vessels, contract only when stimulated by signal molecules. Other smooth muscles contract spontaneously.

3. **Cardiac muscle** is found in the heart. The powerful, rhythmic contractions of cardiac muscle pump blood to all body tissues. Cardiac muscle consists of interconnected cells. Groups of neighboring cells contract all at once, stimulating adjacent groups of cells to contract.

(continued on next page)

Read each question and write your answer in the space provided.

SKILL: Reading Effectively

1. Compare the concentration of *connective tissue* cells found in bone with the concentration of those found in blood.

_____

_____

_____

2. Compare voluntary and involuntary muscle.

_____

_____

_____

SKILL: Recognizing Similarities and Differences

3. Identify the type of body tissue described. Write *epithelial tissue, nervous tissue, connective tissue, skeletal muscle, smooth muscle,* or *cardiac muscle* on the line.

a. _____ its slow, long-lasting contractions cannot consciously be controlled

b. _____ carries information about stimuli throughout the body

c. _____ moves bones in the trunk and limbs

d. _____ lines most body surfaces

e. _____ insulates the body

f. _____ is found in the heart

g. _____ protects other tissues from dehydration

h. _____ holds structures together

i. _____ is constantly being replaced as cells die

j. _____ is made of nerve cells and their supporting cells

k. _____ pumps blood to all body tissues

Circle the letter of the word or phrase that best completes the statement.

4. Fat, cartilage, bone, and tendons are types of
   a. nervous tissue.
   b. cardiac muscle.
   c. epithelial tissue.
   d. connective tissue.

38 **ACTIVE READING**

Introduction to Body Structure

▶ Section 38-2: Skeletal System

Read the passage below, which is reproduced from page 861 of your textbook. Answer the questions that follow.

Bones are made of a hard outer shell of compact bone surrounding a porous inner core of spongy bone. Compact bone is a dense connective tissue that provides a great deal of support. Spongy bone is a loosely structured network of separated connective tissue. Some cavities in spongy bone are filled with a soft tissue called **bone marrow.** Red bone marrow begins the production of all blood cells and platelets. The hollow interior of long bones is filled with yellow bone marrow. Yellow bone marrow consists mostly of fat which stores energy. Bones are surrounded and protected by a tough exterior membrane called the **periosteum.** The periosteum contains many blood vessels that supply nutrients to bones.

Read each question and write your answer in the space provided.

SKILL: Reading Effectively

1. Where does the production of blood cells and platelets begin?

_____

_____

2. What does yellow bone marrow consist of?

_____

_____

3. What does the *periosteum* supply to bones?

_____

_____

(continued on next page)

4. Label the following parts of the diagram: bone marrow, compact bone, periosteum, and spongy bone.

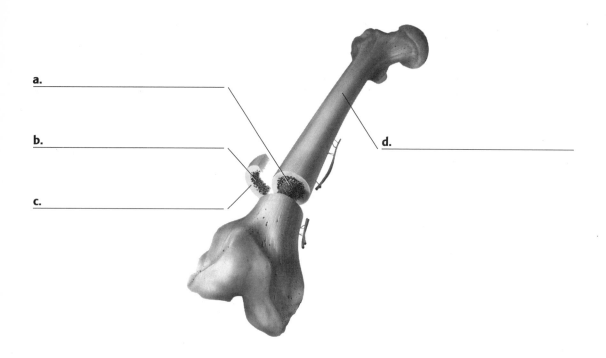

a. _____

b. _____

c. _____

d. _____

5. In the spaces provided, describe the differences between compact bone and spongy bone.

a. Compact bone: _____

_____

b. Spongy bone: _____

_____

Circle the letter of the word or phrase that best completes the statement.

6. The interior of long bones is filled with yellow bone marrow, which consists mostly of
   a. nervous tissue.
   b. energy-storing fat.
   c. red blood cells.
   d. platelets.

CHAPTER

38 **ACTIVE READING**

Introduction to Body Structure

▶ Section 38-3: Muscular System

Read the passage below, which is reproduced from page 867 of your textbook. Answer the questions that follow.

Muscles contain some connective tissue, which holds muscle cells together and provides elasticity. Muscle tissue also contains large amounts of protein filaments. These protein filaments, called **actin** and **myosin,** enable muscles to contract. Other characteristics of muscle tissue include the ability to stretch or expand and the ability to respond to stimuli, such as signal molecules released by nerve cells.

Skeletal muscle tissue consists of many parallel, elongated cells called muscle fibers. Each muscle fiber is made of small cylindrical structures called **myofibrils.** Myofibrils have alternating light and dark bands that produce a characteristic striated, or striped, appearance when viewed under a microscope. In the center of each light band is a structure called a Z line, which anchors actin filaments. The area between two Z lines is called a **sarcomere.** Thus, a myofibril is a grouping of sarcomeres linked end to end. Each sarcomere contains overlapping thin and thick protein filaments that move and interact with each other. The thin filaments are actin, and the thick filaments are myosin.

Read each question and write your answer in the space provided.

SKILL: Reading Effectively

1. What is the function of the connective tissue found in muscle tissue, as described in the first sentence of the passage?

_____

_____

2. How are *actin* and *myosin* similar?

_____

_____

3. What effect do signal molecules released by nerve cells have on muscle tissue?

_____

_____

4. How are *sarcomeres*, *actin*, and *myosin* related?

_____

5. The figure illustrates the structure of a skeletal muscle. Label the following parts of the figure: *actin, myofibrin, myosin, sarcomere,* and *Z line.*

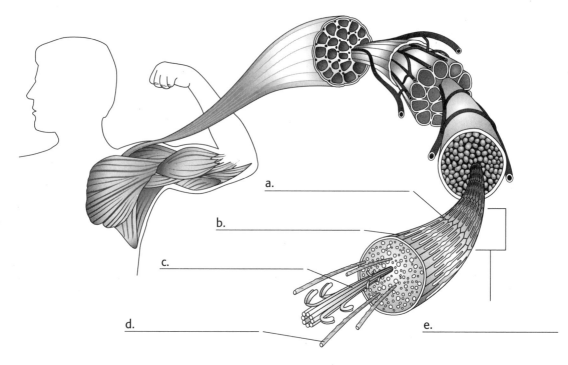

a. _____

b. _____

c. _____

d. _____

e. _____

6. In the spaces provided, define the skeletal muscle parts listed in the figure above.

a. Actin: _____

_____

b. Myofibrin: _____

_____

c. Myosin: _____

_____

d. Sarcomere: _____

_____

e. Z line: _____

_____

Circle the letter of the word or phrase that best completes the statement.

7. Muscle tissue contains

   a. protein filaments.   **c.** white blood cells.
   b. connective tissue.   **d.** Both (a) and (b)

CHAPTER

38 **ACTIVE READING**

Introduction to Body Structure

► Section 38-4: Skin, Hair, and Nails

Read the passage below, which is reproduced from page 874 of your textbook. Answer the questions that follow.

The most common skin problem for teenagers is acne, a chronic inflammatory condition that involves the skin's oil-producing glands. Oil glands in the dermis release **sebum,** an oily secretion that lubricates the skin. Sebum is released through ducts, or pores, into nearby hair follicles. These oil glands are especially active during adolescence. Acne is caused by excessive secretion of sebum, which blocks pores with oil, dirt, and bacteria. Makeup and other cosmetic products can contribute to clogging. As a result, the surrounding tissue becomes infected and inflamed, and the pores accumulate pus, producing pimples. Serious acne may need to be treated using antibiotics. Although acne cannot be prevented, it can usually be managed with proper skin care.

Read each question and write your answer in the space provided.

SKILL: Reading Effectively

1. What word is defined in the first sentence of the passage? What does this word mean?

   _____

   _____

2. What Key Term is defined in the second sentence? What does this word mean?

   _____

   _____

3. What synonym for ducts is provided in the third sentence?

   _____

   _____

Circle the letter of the word or phrase that best completes the statement.

4. Sebum blocks pores with all of the following EXCEPT

   a. pus.   **c.** bacteria.

   b. dirt.   **d.** oil.

CHAPTER

39 **ACTIVE READING**

Circulatory and Respiratory Systems

▶ Section 39-1: The Circulatory System

Read the passage below, which is reproduced from page 883 of your textbook. Answer the questions that follow.

Blood circulates through the body through a network of vessels. **Arteries** are blood vessels that carry blood away from the heart. The blood passes from arteries into a network of smaller arteries called arterioles. Eventually, the blood is pushed through to the capillaries.

Capillaries are tiny blood vessels that allow the exchange of gases, nutrients, hormones, and other molecules traveling in the blood. The molecules are exchanged with the cells of the body. From the capillaries, the blood flows into small vessels called venules before emptying into larger vessels called veins. **Veins** are blood vessels that carry the blood back to the heart.

With each contraction, the heart forcefully ejects blood into the arteries. To accommodate each forceful pulse of blood, an artery's wall expands and then returns to its original size. Elastic fibers in the walls of arteries allow arteries to expand.

The wall of an artery is made up of three layers of tissue. The innermost layer is a thin layer of epithelial tissue called the endothelium. The endothelium is made up of a single layer of cells. Surrounding the endothelium is a layer of smooth muscle tissue with elastic fibers. Finally, a protective layer of connective tissue with elastic fibers wraps around the smooth muscle tissue.

Read each question and write your answer in the space provided.

SKILL: Reading Effectively

1. What information does the first sentence of the passage convey to the reader?

_____

_____

2. The suffix *-ole* means "small or little." How would knowing the common meaning of this word part help you define the term *arteriole*?

_____

_____

3. What definition is given in the first sentence of the second paragraph?

_____

_____

4. The passage describes five types of blood vessels. In what order would blood leaving the heart flow through these blood vessels?

_____

_____

5. What is the function of the elastic fibers found in an artery's walls?

_____

_____

SKILL: Interpreting Graphics

6. The figure shows blood vessels of the circulatory system. Insert the following labels on the figure: arterioles, artery, capillaries, connective tissue, endothelium, smooth muscle, vein, and venules.

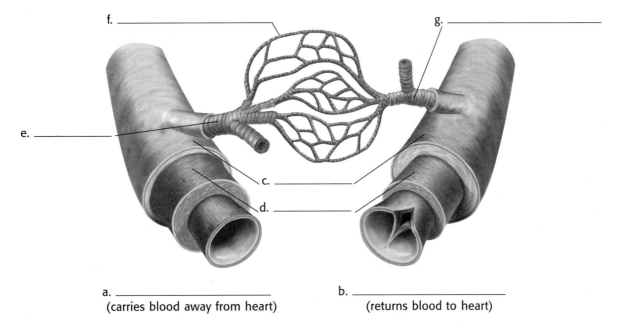

f. _____   g. _____

e. _____

c. _____

d. _____

a. _____   b. _____
(carries blood away from heart)   (returns blood to heart)

Circle the letter of the word or phrase that best completes the statement.

7. All of the following substances are exchanged in the capillaries EXCEPT
   a. nutrients.
   b. water.
   c. hormones.
   d. gases.

Circulatory and Respiratory Systems

▶ Section 39-2: The Heart

Read the passage below, which is reproduced from page 892 of your textbook. Answer the questions that follow.

Doctors routinely measure a patient's blood pressure. **Blood pressure** is the force exerted by blood as it moves through blood vessels. Blood pressure readings provide information about the condition of the arteries. Blood pressure is measured with a device called a sphygmomanometer. The first number, the systolic pressure, tells how much pressure is exerted when the heart contracts and blood flows through the arteries. The second number, the diastolic pressure, tells how much pressure is exerted when the heart relaxes. Blood pressure is expressed in terms of millimeters of mercury (mm Hg) and is usually reported as the systolic pressure written over the diastolic pressure.

Normal blood pressure values range from 100 to 130 for systolic pressure and from 70 to 90 for diastolic pressure.

Read each question and write your answer in the space provided.

SKILL: Reading Effectively

1. What information do *blood pressure* numbers provide about a patient and how is this information helpful to physicians?

_____

_____

_____

2. How are systolic and diastolic pressure different?

_____

_____

_____

Circle the letter of the word or phrase that best completes the statement.

3. Thermometer is to body temperature as sphygmomanometer is to
   a. blood type.   **c.** respiratory rate.
   b. heart rate.   **d.** blood pressure.

CHAPTER
39 ACTIVE READING

─Circulatory and Respiratory Systems

▶ Section 39-3: The Respiratory System

Read the passage below, which is reproduced from page 895 of your textbook. Answer the questions that follow.

All of the organs and tissues that function in the exchange of gases make up the respiratory system.

A breath of air enters the respiratory system through the nose or mouth. Air is made up of many gases. About 21 percent of air is oxygen gas. Hairs in your nose filter dust and particles out of the air. Tissues that line the nasal cavity moisten and warm the air.

From the nose, air passes through a muscular tube in the upper throat called the **pharynx,** which serves as a passageway for food and air. The air continues on through another passageway for air, called the **larynx,** or voice box located in the neck. A flap of tissue, the epiglottis, covers the opening to the larynx when you swallow food and liquids, preventing food and liquids from passing into your lungs.

From the larynx the air passes into the **trachea,** a long, straight tube in the chest cavity. The trachea, or windpipe, divides into two smaller tubes, the **bronchi,** which lead to the lungs. Within the lung, the bronchi divide into smaller and smaller tubes called bronchioles. The smallest bronchioles end in clusters of air sacs called **alveoli,** where gases are actually exchanged.

Read each question and write your answer in the space provided.

SKILL: Reading Effectively

1. What is the function of the respiratory system?

_____

_____

2. What relationship exists between oxygen gas and air?

_____

_____

_____

3. How does the epiglottis prevent choking?

_____

_____

4. Where does gas exchange actually occur?

_____

SKILL: Interpreting Graphics

5. The figure illustrates the parts of the respiratory system. Label the following parts of this system: alveoli, bronchi, bronchioles, capillaries, larynx, lung, pharynx, and trachea.

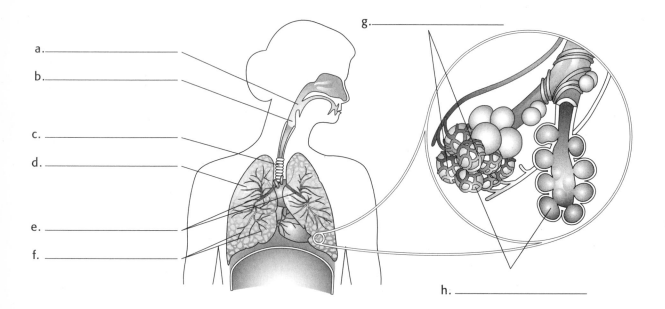

a. _____

b. _____

c. _____

d. _____

e. _____

f. _____

g. _____

h. _____

Circle the letter of the word or phrase that best completes the statement.

6. The function of nasal hair is to

   a. warm air entering the respiratory system.
   b. expel waste gases.
   c. filter foreign particles from incoming air.
   d. Both (a) and (b)

CHAPTER
40 **ACTIVE READING**

─Digestive and Excretory Systems

▶ Section 40-1: Your Body's Need for Food

Read the passage below, which is reproduced from page 908 of your textbook. Answer the questions that follow.

Your body uses energy to move, to grow, and even to lie still or sleep. The amount of energy you need depends on many factors, including your age, gender, rate of growth, and level of physical activity.

You obtain energy from the nutrients in the foods and beverages you consume. A **nutrient** is a substance needed by the body for energy, growth, repair, and maintenance. Nutrients in food and beverages include carbohydrates, lipids, proteins, vitamins, and minerals. Each nutrient plays a different role in keeping your body healthy. Water in food and beverages is also needed to maintain a healthy body.

Large molecules in food must be broken down in order to be absorbed into the blood and carried to cells throughout the body. The process of breaking food down into molecules the body can use is called **digestion.** Your cells then break the chemical bonds of digested food molecules and use the energy that is released to make ATP during the process of cellular respiration.

Energy available in food is measured using a unit called a calorie. A **calorie** is the amount of heat energy needed to raise the temperature of 1 g of water 1°C (1.8°F). The greater the number of calories in a quantity of food, the more energy the food contains. Since a calorie represents a very small amount of energy, nutritionists use a unit called the Calorie (with a capital C), which is equal to 1,000 calories. On food labels, the word *calorie* represents Calories (1,000 calories).

Read each question and write your answer in the space provided.

SKILL: Reading Effectively

1. What factors determine the amount of energy your body needs?

_____

_____

_____

2. What are *nutrients*?

_____

_____

3. What *nutrients* are contained in the food and beverages you consume?

_____

_____

4. In addition to *nutrients* what other substance does the body need?

_____

5. What is *digestion*?

_____

_____

6. Why is it necessary to break down certain *nutrients*?

_____

_____

_____

_____

7. What occurs when the chemical bonds of digested food molecules are broken?

_____

_____

8. How are a *calorie* and a Calorie alike? How do they differ?

_____

_____

_____

Circle the letter of the word or phrase that best completes the statement.

9. The fewer the number of calories in a quantity of food, the
   a. more energy the food contains.
   b. more heat the food contains.
   c. less energy the food contains.
   d. Both (a) and (b)

CHAPTER 40 — ACTIVE READING

Digestive and Excretory Systems

▶ Section 40-2: Digestion

Read the passage below, which is reproduced from page 917 of your textbook. Answer the questions that follow.

Food passes from the stomach into the small intestine when a sphincter between the two organs opens. The small intestine is a coiled tubular organ about 6 m (19.8 ft) long that is connected with the stomach and that functions mainly in the digestion and absorption of nutrients. The word *small* refers to the small diameter—not length—of the small intestine, as compared to the diameter of the large intestine.

The first part of the small intestine, the duodenum, receives secretions from the pancreas, liver, and gallbladder. Cells that line the small intestine and the pancreas secrete digestive enzymes involved in completing the digestion of carbohydrates into monosaccharides, proteins into amino acids, and lipids into fatty acids and glycerol.

Before fats can be digested by pancreatic enzymes called **lipases,** the fats must first be treated with bile, a greenish fluid produced by the liver. Bile breaks up fat globules into tiny droplets, a process called emulsification. The gall bladder, a green muscular sac attached to the liver, stores bile until it is needed in the small intestine.

Most absorption occurs in the small intestine. The lining of the small intestine is covered with fine, fingerlike projections called **villi** (singular form *villus*), each of which is too small to be seen with the naked eye. In turn, the cells covering each villus have projections on their outer surface called microvilli. The villi and microvilli greatly increase the area available for absorption of nutrients, including vitamins and minerals.

Read each question and write your answer in the space provided.

SKILL: Reading Effectively

1. According to the passage, what are two main functions of the small intestine?

_____

_____

2. In what way is the small intestine *small*?

_____

_____

3. What relationship exists between the small intestine and the duodenum?

_____

_____

4. Which organs secrete fluids into the small intestine?

_____

5. What is the function of the digestive enzymes secreted by cells lining the small intestine?

_____

_____

_____

_____

6. What are *lipases*?

_____

7. What occurs during emulsification?

_____

_____

8. What relationship exists between bile and the gall bladder?

_____

_____

9. What relationship exists between *villi* and microvilli?

_____

_____

An analogy is a comparison. Circle the letter of the word or phrase that best completes the analogy.

10. Proteins are to amino acids as lipids are to
   a. monosaccharides.
   b. glycerol.
   c. lipases.
   d. Both (a) and (b)

CHAPTER
40
ACTIVE READING

Digestive and Excretory Systems

▶ Section 40-3: Excretion

Read the passage below, which is reproduced from page 920 of your textbook. Answer the questions that follow.

In order to maintain a healthy state, the body must get rid of wastes. Food residues are eliminated from the body in the form of feces. Other wastes produced as a result of metabolic reactions that occur in the body must also be eliminated. For example, water and carbon dioxide are produced during cellular respiration. During the metabolism of proteins and nucleic acids, a toxic, nitrogen-containing waste called ammonia is formed. The body must quickly remove these wastes and maintain osmotic balance and pH by either excreting or conserving salts and water. **Excretion** is the process that rids the body of toxic chemicals, excess water, salts, and carbon dioxide and maintains osmotic and pH balance.

Read each question and write your answer in the space provided.

SKILL: Reading Effectively

1. What metabolic reactions produce wastes that must be eliminated by the body?

   _____

   _____

2. What are two ways that the body can remove wastes and maintain osmotic balance and pH?

   _____

   _____

3. What is *excretion*?

   _____

   _____

Circle the letter of the word or phrase that best completes the statement.

4. Food residues are eliminated from the body in the form of
   a. ammonia.   **c.** feces.
   b. salts.   **d.** Both (a) and (b)

The Body's Defenses

▶ Section 41-1: Nonspecific Defenses

Read the passage below, which is reproduced from page 933 of your textbook. Answer the questions that follow.

When the body is invaded, four important nonspecific defenses take action: the inflammatory response; the temperature response; proteins that kill or inhibit pathogens; and white blood cells, which attack and kill pathogens.

Inflammatory Response: Injury or local infection, such as a cut or a scrape, causes an inflammatory response. An **inflammatory response** is a series of events that suppress infection and speed recovery. Imagine that a splinter has punctured your finger, creating an entrance for pathogens. Infected or injured cells in your finger release chemicals, including histamine. **Histamine** causes local blood vessels to dilate, increasing blood flow to the area. Increased blood flow brings white blood cells to the infection site, where they can attack pathogens. The increased blood flow also causes swelling and redness in the infected area. The whitish liquid, or pus, associated with some infections contains white blood cells, dead cells, and dead pathogens.

Temperature Response: When the body begins its fight against pathogens, body temperature increases several degrees above the normal value of about 37°C (99°F). This higher temperature is called a fever, and it is a common symptom of illness that shows the body is responding to an infection. Fever is helpful because many disease-causing bacteria do not grow well at high temperatures.

Read each question and write your answer in the space provided.

SKILL: Reading Effectively

1. What four nonspecific defenses are caused by pathogens invading the body?

_____

_____

_____

2. What is an *inflammatory response?*

_____

3. What three effects does increased blood flow have on an infection site?

_____

_____

_____

4. What effect does fever have on many disease-causing bacteria?

_____

_____

SKILL: Interpreting Graphics

5. The figure illustrates the inflammatory response. On the lines below, describe what is occurring in each part of the figure.

Part a   **Part b**   **Part c**

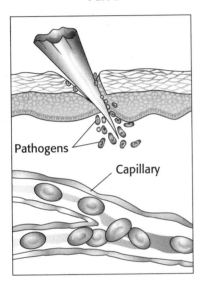
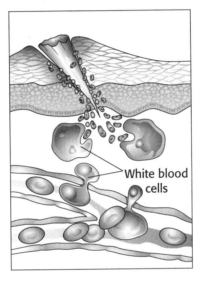
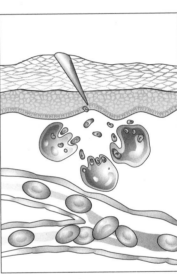

Pathogens

Capillary

White blood cells

Part a: _____

_____

Part b: _____

_____

Part c: _____

_____

Circle the letter of the word or phrase that best completes the statement.

6. Release of the chemical histamine causes
   a. the production of white blood cells.
   b. a decrease in blood flow.
   c. a decrease in body temperature.
   d. blood vessels to dilate.

The Body's Defenses

► Section 41-2: Immune Response

Read the passage below, which is reproduced from page 935 of your textbook. Answer the questions that follow.

White blood cells are produced in bone marrow and circulate in blood and lymph. Of the 100 trillion cells in your body, about 2 trillion are white blood cells. Four main kinds of white blood cells participate in the immune response: macrophages, cytotoxic T cells, B cells, and helper T cells. Each kind of cell has a different function. **Macrophages** consume pathogens and infected cells. **Cytotoxic T cells** attack and kill infected cells. **B cells** label invaders for later destruction by macrophages. **Helper T cells** activate both cytotoxic T cells and B cells. These four kinds of white blood cells interact to remove pathogens from the body.

Read each question and write your answer in the space provided.

SKILL: Organizing Information

1. Write the type of white blood cell described by the phrase.

   a. _____ label invaders for later destruction

   b. _____ consume pathogens

   c. _____ kill infected cells

   d. _____ activate B cells

   e. _____ consume infected cells

   f. _____ activate cytotoxic T cells

Circle the letter of the word or phrase that best completes the statement.

2. A ratio of white blood cells to body cells shows one white blood cell to
   a. 10 body cells.
   b. 50 body cells.
   c. 1,000 body cells.
   d. 5,000,000 body cells.

The Body's Defenses

▶ Section 41-3: Disease Transmission and Prevention

Read the passage below, which is reproduced from page 938 of your textbook. Answer the questions that follow.

The German physician Robert Koch (1843–1910) established a procedure for diagnosing causes of infection. In his research with anthrax, Koch developed the following four-step procedure, known as **Koch's postulates,** as a guide for identifying specific pathogens. Biologists have used Koch's postulates to identify many pathogens.

1. The pathogen must be found in an animal with the disease and not in a healthy animal.

2. The pathogen must be isolated from the sick animal and grown in a laboratory culture.

3. When the isolated pathogen is injected into a healthy animal, the animal must develop the disease.

4. The pathogen should be taken from the second animal and grown in a laboratory culture. The pathogen should be the same as the original pathogen.

Read each question and write your answer in the space provided.

SKILL: Reading Effectively

1. What is indicated when, in spite of being injected with a pathogen isolated from a sick animal, another animal remains healthy?

_____

_____

Circle the letter of the word or phrase that best completes the statement.

2. According to Koch's postulates, a pathogen can be considered to cause a particular disease if the pathogen is
   a. found in an animal with the disease.
   b. lacking in healthy animals.
   c. found in all members of the same species.
   d. Both (a) and (b)

CHAPTER
41 **ACTIVE READING**

The Body's Defenses

▶ Section 41-4: Disorders of the Immune System

Read the passage below, which is reproduced from page 943 of your textbook. Answer the questions that follow.

You can become infected with HIV if you receive HIV-infected white blood cells, which are present in many body fluids. The most common method of HIV transmission is through sexual contact. Because semen, vaginal fluid, and mucous membranes may contain HIV, both males and females can become infected with HIV during vaginal, anal, or oral intercourse. Use of a latex condom during intercourse reduces but does not eliminate the risk of getting or spreading HIV.

HIV can be passed between drug users who share a hypodermic needle if HIV-infected blood remains in the needle or syringe. In the late 1970s and early 1980s, many people became infected with HIV after receiving transfusions of HIV-contaminated blood. This is very unlikely now because blood made available for transfusion is tested for HIV. In addition, pregnant or nursing mothers can pass HIV to their infants through breast milk and blood.

HIV is not transmitted through the air, by toilet seats, by kissing or handshaking, or by any other medium where HIV-infected white blood cells could not survive. Although HIV has been found in tears, saliva, and urine, these body fluids usually contain too few HIV particles to cause an infection. Insects such as mosquitoes and ticks do not transmit HIV because they do not carry infected white blood cells.

Read each question and write your answer in the space provided.

SKILL: Reading Effectively

1. What is the most common method of HIV transmission?

_____

_____

_____

_____

2. Why is it possible for either a male or female to become infected with HIV during vaginal, anal, or oral intercourse?

_____

_____

3. How can HIV be passed between drug users?

_____

_____

_____

4. Why is it unlikely that a person who receives a blood transfusion today will become infected with HIV?

_____

_____

5. Why isn't HIV transmitted through the air?

_____

_____

_____

Circle the letter of the word or phrase that best completes the statement.

6. HIV cannot be transmitted by
   a. handshaking.
   b. breast milk.
   c. blood transfusions.
   d. oral intercourse.

CHAPTER
(42) **ACTIVE READING**

Nervous System

▶ Section 42-1: Neurons and Nerve Impulses

Read the passage below, which is reproduced from page 952 of your textbook. Answer the questions that follow.

A neuron's unique structure enables it to conduct electrical signals called nerve impulses. Neurons communicate by transmitting nerve impulses to body tissues and organs, including muscles, glands, and other neurons. **Dendrites,** which extend from the cell body of the neuron, are the "antennae" of the neuron. Dendrites receive information from other cells. The cell body collects information from the dendrites, relays this information to other parts of the neuron, and maintains the general functioning of the neuron. An **axon** is a long extension of the cytoplasm that conducts nerve impulses. The end of an axon is called an axon terminal. When the neuron transmits a nerve impulse to other cells, the nerve impulse leaves from axon terminals.

Nervous tissue consists mostly of neurons and their supporting cells. Bundles of neurons are called **nerves,** which contain the axons of many different neurons.

Read each question and write your answer in the space provided.

SKILL: Reading Effectively

1. How do neurons communicate?

   _____

   _____

2. What is the function of a neuron's *dendrites*?

   _____

   _____

3. What is the function of a neuron's cell body?

   _____

   _____

   _____

4. What is an *axon*?

_____

_____

5. How are *axons* and *nerves* related?

_____

_____

Circle the letter of the word or phrase that best completes the statement.

6. A neuron is able to conduct electrical signals, or nerve impulses, due to its unique

   a. size.

   b. location.

   c. structure.

   d. Both (a) and (b)

Nervous System

▶ Section 42-2: Structures of the Nervous System

Read the passage below, which is reproduced from page 959 of your textbook. Answer the questions that follow.

The brain consists of three major parts—the cerebrum, the cerebellum, and the brain stem.

Cerebrum: The **cerebrum** is the largest part of the brain. The capacity for learning, memory, perception, and intellectual functioning resides in the cerebrum. The cerebrum has a folded outer layer with many bumps and grooves. A long, deep groove down the center of the brain divides the cerebrum into right and left halves, or hemispheres. The cerebral hemispheres communicate through a connecting band of axons called the corpus callosum. In general, the left cerebral hemisphere receives sensations from and controls the movements of the right side of the body. The right cerebral hemisphere receives sensations from and controls the movements of the left side of the body.

Most sensory and motor processing occurs in the cerebral cortex, the folded, thin outer layer of the cerebrum. The cerebral cortex contains about 10 percent of the brain's neurons. The folds on the outer surface of the cerebrum accommodate the large surface area of the cerebral cortex. The cerebral cortex is primarily involved with the functioning of sensory systems.

Cerebellum: Located at the posterior base of the brain, the **cerebellum** regulates balance, posture, and movement. The cerebellum smoothes and coordinates ongoing movements, such as walking, by timing the contraction of skeletal muscles. The cerebellum integrates and responds to information about body position from the cerebrum and the spinal cord to control balance and posture.

Brain stem: At the base of the brain is the stalklike **brain stem.** The brain stem is a collection of structures leading down to the spinal cord and connecting the cerebral hemispheres with the cerebellum. The lower brain stem consists of the midbrain, the pons, and the medulla oblongata. These structures relay information throughout the central nervous system and play an important role in homeostasis by regulating vital functions such as heart rate, breathing rate, body temperature, and sleep.

(continued on next page)

Read each question and write your answer in the space provided.

SKILL: Reading Effectively

1. Using Key Terms from the passage above, write the name of the brain part described by each phrase.

a. _____ regulates balance

b. _____ leads to the spinal cord

c. _____ largest part of the brain

d. _____ divided into two hemispheres

e. _____ pons is located here

f. _____ contains the corpus callosum

g. _____ responds to information about body position

h. _____ capacity for learning resides here

i. _____ breathing rate is regulated here

j. _____ located at the base of the brain

k. _____ has a folded layer with many bumps and grooves

l. _____ regulates posture

m. _____ left side controls right side of the body

n. _____ medulla oblongata located here

o. _____ times contractions of the skeletal muscles

p. _____ cerebral cortex is located here

q. _____ located at the posterior base of the brain

r. _____ heart rate is regulated here

s. _____ capacity for intellectual function resides here

An analogy is a comparison. Circle the letter of the word or phrase that best completes the analogy.

2. Cerebellum is to movement as cerebrum is to
   a. breathing.
   b. walking.
   c. sleeping.
   d. perception.

CHAPTER

42 **ACTIVE READING**

Nervous System

▶ Section 42-3: Sensory Systems

Read the passage below, which is reproduced from page 967 of your textbook. Answer the questions that follow.

Your ears convert the energy in sound waves to electrical signals that can be interpreted by your brain. Sound waves enter through the ear canal and strike the tympanic membrane, or eardrum, causing the tympanic membrane to vibrate. Behind the eardrum, three small bones of the middle ear—the anvil, hammer, and stirrup—transfer the vibrations to a fluid-filled chamber within the inner ear. This chamber, called the **cochlea,** is coiled like a snail's shell, and it contains mechanoreceptors called hair cells. When hair cells are stimulated, they generate nerve impulses in the auditory nerve. The electrical signals travel to the brain stem via the auditory nerve. The thalamus relays the information to the temporal lobe of the cerebral cortex, where the auditory information is processed.

The ears not only enable you to hear but also help you maintain your balance. The **semicircular canals** are fluid-filled chambers in the inner ear that contain hair cells. Clusters of these hair cells respond to changes in head position with respect to gravity. When your head moves or rotates, the hair cells bend according to the magnitude and direction of the fluid's movement and send electrical signals to the brain. Signals generated by the hair cells enable the brain to determine the orientation and position of the head.

Read each question and write your answer in the space provided.

SKILL: Reading Effectively

1. According to the passage, what are two functions of the ear?

_____

_____

2. How does energy change form in the ear?

_____

_____

3. What causes the tympanic membrane to vibrate?

_____

_____

_____

4. What is the *cochlea*?

_____

_____

5. How do vibrations reach the *cochlea*?

_____

_____

_____

6. What occurs when hair cells are stimulated?

_____

_____

7. What are *semicircular canals*?

_____

_____

8. How do the *semicircular canals* help you maintain balance?

_____

_____

_____

_____

Circle the letter of the word or phrase that best completes the statement.

9. The semicircular canals and cochlea are alike in that both are
   a. located in the inner ear.
   b. fluid-filled chambers.
   c. convert sound energy to electrical signals.
   d. Both (a) and (b)

Nervous System

▶ **Section 42-4: Drugs and the Nervous System**

Read the passage below, which is reproduced from page 973 of your textbook. Answer the questions that follow.

Alcohol, found in wine, beer, and liquor, is a depressant that produces a sense of well-being when taken in small amounts. A **depressant** is a drug that generally decreases the activity of the central nervous system. As more alcohol is consumed, reaction time increases, and coordination, judgment, and speech become impaired. This produces a state of intoxication known as being "drunk."

Alcohol is absorbed into the blood through the stomach and small intestine. Alcohol alters neurons throughout the nervous system, changing the shape of receptor proteins. Altered receptor proteins may become more or less sensitive to regular stimuli. Such widespread changes in receptor proteins have various effects on normal brain functioning.

Read each question and write your answer in the space provided.

SKILL: Reading Effectively

1. What is a *depressant*?

_____

_____

2. What occurs as the amount of alcohol taken into the body increases?

_____

_____

3. How does alcohol enter the bloodstream?

_____

_____

Circle the letter of the word or phrase that best completes the statement.

4. Alcohol is found in all of the following EXCEPT

    a. cola.   **c.** liquor.

    b. wine.   **d.** beer.

CHAPTER

43 **ACTIVE READING**

Hormones and the Endocrine System

▶ Section 43-1: Hormones

Read the passage below, which is reproduced from page 983 of your textbook. Answer the questions that follow.

A gland is an organ whose cells secrete materials into other regions of the body. **Endocrine glands** are ductless organs that secrete hormones directly into either the bloodstream or the fluid around cells (extracellular fluid). In addition to the endocrine glands, several other organs contain cells that secrete hormones. These organs include the brain, stomach, small intestine, kidney, liver, and heart. Endocrine glands and tissues collectively make up the endocrine system. The endocrine system coordinates all of the body's sources of hormones.

Some organs, such as the pancreas, are both endocrine and exocrine glands. Exocrine glands deliver substances through ducts. The exocrine part of the pancreas produces digestive enzymes and delivers them to the small intestine through ducts. The endocrine part of the pancreas secretes two hormones into the bloodstream that regulate blood glucose levels.

Read each question and write your answer in the space provided.

SKILL: Reading Effectively

1. What is the purpose of the first sentence of this passage?

_____

_____

2. What are *endocrine glands*?

_____

_____

_____

3. What is a term for "fluid around cells"?

_____

_____

4. Other than the *endocrine glands*, what organs contain cells that secrete hormones?

_____

_____

5. Compare the function of the exocrine and endocrine parts of the pancreas.

_____

_____

_____

_____

_____

Circle the letter of the word or phrase that best completes the statement.

6. All of the following are types of glands except the
   a. bloodstream.
   b. brain.
   c. heart.
   d. kidneys.

Hormones and the Endocrine System

▶ **Section 43-2: How Hormones Work**

Read the passage below, which is reproduced from page 986 of your textbook. Answer the questions that follow.

When a hormone binds to a specific receptor on a target cell, the hormone is acting as a first messenger. Hormones bring the target cell a message. What happens after the hormone binds, however, depends on the type of hormone. Because amino-acid-based hormones are not fat soluble, most bind to cell membrane receptors in the following manner:

Step 1: When an amino-acid-based hormone binds to a receptor protein, the shape of the receptor protein changes. For example, when glucagon, an amino-acid-based hormone made in the pancreas, binds to receptors on liver cells, the receptors change their shape.

Step 2: This change in shape eventually results in the activation of a **second messenger,** a molecule that passes the message from the first messenger (the hormone) to the cell. For example, when glucagon binds to a receptor, an enzyme is activated that converts ATP to a second messenger called cyclic AMP (cAMP).

Step 3: The second messenger then activates or deactivates certain enzymes in a cascade fashion. That is, one enzyme activates another enzyme, which activates another, and so on.

Step 4: Eventually the activity of the target cell is changed by the final enzyme in the cascade—even though the hormone never entered the cell! In the case of glucagons, the AMP molecules alter the activity of liver cells by activating a series of enzymes that break down glycogen into many individual glucose molecules.

Read each question and write your answer in the space provided.

SKILL: Reading Effectively

1. Why do most amino-acid-based hormones bind to cell membrane receptors?

_____

_____

2. What happens when an amino-acid-based hormone binds to a receptor protein?

_____

_____

3. What is glucagon?

_____

_____

4. What is a _second messenger_?

_____

_____

5. What causes the activation of a _second messenger_?

_____

_____

6. What happens when glucagon binds to a receptor?

_____

_____

7. What effect does a _second messenger_ have on its target cell?

_____

_____

Circle the letter of the word or phrase that best completes the statement.

8. When glucagon binds to a protein receptor, ATP is converted to
   a. a first messenger.
   b. cyclic AMP.
   c. glucose molecules.
   d. a target cell.

Hormones and the Endocrine System

▶ **Section 43-3: The Major Endocrine Glands of the Body**

Read the passage below, which is reproduced from page 990 of your textbook. Answer the questions that follow.

Feedback mechanisms fine-tune the levels of hormones in circulation, but two endocrine glands control the initial release of many hormones. The hypothalamus and the pituitary gland together serve as a major control center for the rest of the endocrine system.

The **hypothalamus** is the area of the brain that coordinates the activities of the nervous and endocrine systems and controls many body functions, including body temperature, blood pressure, and emotions. The hypothalamus receives information about external and internal conditions from other brain regions. The hypothalamus responds to both of these signals from the nervous system and the blood concentrations of circulating hormones. The hypothalamus responds by issuing instructions—in the form of hormones—to the pituitary gland.

The **pituitary gland** is an endocrine gland suspended from the hypothalamus by a short stalk. The pituitary gland secretes many hormones, including some that control endocrine glands elsewhere in the body. The nerve cells in the hypothalamus make at least six hormones that are released into a special network of blood vessels between the hypothalamus and the pituitary gland. Some of these hormones are "releasing" hormones, which cause the front part of the pituitary gland (the anterior pituitary gland) to make and then release a corresponding pituitary hormone. "Inhibiting" hormones signal the anterior pituitary gland to stop secretion of one of its hormones.

Read each question and write your answer in the space provided.

SKILL: Reading Effectively

1. What is the main function of the *hypothalamus* and *pituitary gland*?

_____

_____

(continued on next page)

2. What is the *hypothalamus*?

_____

_____

3. What body functions are controlled by the *hypothalamus*?

_____

_____

4. How does the *hypothalamus* receive information about external and internal conditions of the body?

_____

_____

_____

5. How does the *hypothalamus* respond to such signals?

_____

_____

6. Where is the *pituitary gland* located?

_____

_____

7. How are "releasing" and "inhibiting" hormones alike? How do they differ?

_____

_____

_____

_____

_____

Circle the letter of the word or phrase that best completes the statement.

8. The hypothalamus and pituitary gland control the
   a. actions of the nervous system.
   b. concentrations of blood hormones.
   c. release of many hormones.
   d. Both (a) and (b)

CHAPTER
(44) **ACTIVE READING**

Reproduction and Development

▶ Section 44-1: Male Reproductive System

Read the passage below, which is reproduced from page 1006 of your textbook. Answer the questions that follow.

Sexual reproduction involves the formation of a (diploid) zygote from two (haploid) sex cells, or gametes, through fertilization. The role of a male in sexual reproduction is to produce sperm cells—the male gametes—and to deliver the sperm cells to the female reproductive system to fertilize an egg cell—the female gamete.

Sperm cells are produced in the **testes.** These two egg-shaped structures are the gamete-producing organs of the male reproductive system. The testes are located in the scrotum, an external skin sac. The testes first form inside the abdominal cavity and then move down into the scrotum either before or shortly after birth. The normal body temperature of 37°C (98°F) is too high for sperm to complete development. In the scrotum, the temperature is about 3°C lower than it is in the rest of the body, making the scrotum an ideal location for sperm production.

Read each question and write your answer in the space provided.

SKILL: Reading Effectively

1. What is the main idea of the first sentence of this passage?

_____

_____

2. According to the passage, what is the role of males in reproduction?

_____

_____

3. What are *testes*?

_____

_____

4. What is the scrotum?

_____

_____

5. Where do the *testes* form?

_____

_____

_____

6. Why is the scrotum an ideal location for sperm production?

_____

_____

_____

_____

Circle the letter of the word or phrase that best completes the statement.

7. Another name for testes is
   a. gametes.
   b. scrotum.
   c. testicles.
   d. zygote.

Reproduction and Development

▶ Section 44-2: Female Reproductive System

Read the passage below, which is reproduced from page 1010 of your textbook. Answer the questions that follow.

An ovum is released from an ovary about every 28 days. Cilia sweep the ovum into a fallopian tube. Each **fallopian tube** is a passageway through which an ovum moves from an ovary toward the uterus. Smooth muscles lining the fallopian tubes contract rhythmically, moving the ovum down the tube and toward the uterus. An ovum's journey through a fallopian tube usually takes 3 to 4 days to complete. If the ovum is not fertilized within 24–48 hours, it dies.

The **uterus** is a hollow, muscular organ about the size of a small fist. If fertilization occurs, development will take place in the uterus. During sexual intercourse, sperm are deposited inside the **vagina,** a muscular tube that leads from the outside of the female's body to the entrance of the uterus, called the cervix. During childbirth, a baby passes through the cervix and leaves the mother's body through the vagina.

Read each question and write your answer in the space provided.

SKILL: Reading Effectively

1. How often is an ovum released from an ovary?

_____

2. What is a *fallopian tube*?

_____

_____

3. What causes an ovum to move through a *fallopian tube*?

_____

_____

Circle the letter of the word or phrase that best completes the statement.

4. An ovum moves from an ovary into
   a. a fallopian tube and then the uterus.
   b. the uterus and then the vagina.
   c. the cervix and then the uterus.
   d. a fallopian tube and then the cervix.

Reproduction and Development

▶ Section 44-3: Development

Read the passage below, which is reproduced from page 1014 of your textbook. Answer the questions that follow.

If sperm are present in the female reproductive system within a few days after ovulation, fertilization may occur. To fertilize an ovum, a sperm cell must swim to a fallopian tube, where fertilization usually occurs. During fertilization, a sperm cell penetrates an ovum by releasing enzymes at the tip of its head. These enzymes break down the jelly-like outer layers of the ovum. The head and midpiece of the sperm enter the ovum, and the nuclei of the egg and sperm fuse together. This produces a diploid cell called a zygote. In the first week after fertilization, the zygote undergoes a series of internal divisions known as **cleavage.** Cleavage produces many smaller cells within the zygote. By the time it reaches the uterus, the zygote is a hollow ball of cells called a **blastocyst.** About six days after fertilization, the blastocyst burrows into the lining of the uterus in an event called **implantation.**

Read each question and write your answer in the space provided.

SKILL: Sequencing Information

1. Sequence the events to show the order in which they occur during fertilization, cleavage, and implantation. Write *1* on the line in front of the first event, *2* on the line in front of the second event, and so on.

   a. _____ The zygote undergoes a series of internal divisions.

   b. _____ The head and midpiece of a sperm enter an ovum.

   c. _____ The zygote reaches the uterus.

   d. _____ A sperm cell releases enzymes that break down an ovum's outer layers.

   e. _____ The nuclei of an egg and sperm fuse together.

   f. _____ The blastocyst burrows into the lining of the uterus.

   g. _____ Ovulation occurs.

(continued on next page)

2. What structure must a sperm cell swim toward for fertilization to occur?

_____

_____

3. What type of cell is formed after the nuclei of the egg and sperm fuse together?

_____

_____

Circle the letter of the word or phrase that best answers the question.

4. What occurs as a zygote moves through a fallopian tube?
   a. implantation
   b. cleavage
   c. fertilization
   d. Both (a) and (b)

CHAPTER

44 **ACTIVE READING**

Reproduction and Development

▶ **Section 44-4: Sexually Transmitted Diseases**

Read the passage below, which is reproduced from page 1020 of your textbook. Answer the questions that follow.

Sexually transmitted diseases (STDs) caused by viruses are called viral STDs. Because viruses are not affected by antibiotics, viral STDs cannot be treated and cured using antibiotics. AIDS and genital herpes are two common viral diseases that are transmitted through sexual contact.

AIDS is a fatal disease caused by the human immunodeficiency virus (HIV). Transmission through sexual contact is the most common way that people become exposed to HIV. HIV destroys the immune system of infected individuals by attacking white blood cells. People with AIDS generally die from opportunistic infections that persist only in people with weakened immune systems.

Read each question and write your answer in the space provided.

SKILL: Reading Effectively

1. Why are antibiotics ineffective in treating viral STDs?

_____

_____

_____

_____

2. How are these viral STDs transmitted?

_____

_____

_____

Circle the letter of the word or phrase that best completes the statement.

3. HSV-2 commonly causes

   a. cold sores around and inside the mouth.
   b. destruction of white blood cells.
   c. flulike aches and fever.
   d. Both (a) and (b)

Answer Key

....

CHAPTER 1
Biology and You

SECTION 1-1: THEMES OF BIOLOGY

1. It is a synonym for characteristics that directly precede it.
2. that it is a Key Term, or important word, that is defined in the sentence
3. the passing of traits from parents to offspring
4. It is that children tend to resemble their parents.
5. damage to genes
6. that an egg and sperm are types of sex cells
7. Mutations in body cells cause disruption in the control of cell reproduction, and disruption in the control of cell reproduction causes cancer.
8. c

SECTION 1-2: BIOLOGY IN YOUR WORLD

1. a. decrease or avoid the use of chemical pesticides
   b. increased crop yields
2. genetic engineers
3. Beneficial plant genes are transplanted into plants.
4. food
5. b

SECTION 1-3: THE SCIENTIFIC PROCESS

1. It does not provide a reasonable explanation for what has been observed.
2. They test one or more alternative hypotheses.
3. a set of related hypotheses that have been tested and confirmed many times
4. a. Questions
   b. Predictions
   c. Experimentation
   d. Supported
   e. Rejected
   f. Related
   g. Theory
5. d

CHAPTER 2
Chemistry of Life

SECTION 2-1: NATURE OF MATTER

1. molecule
2. Covalent bonds form when two or more atoms share electrons.

3. a key vocabulary word that is defined in this sentence
4. Covalent bonds that join atoms in molecules are similar to rivets and welds that join girders in a skyscraper.
5. b

SECTION 2-2: WATER AND SOLUTIONS

1. acids and bases; they appear in boldface type
2. Acids are compounds that form hydrogen ions when dissolved in water. Bases are compounds that reduce the concentration of hydrogen ions in a solution.
3. The concentration of hydrogen ions in the solution is increased above that of pure water.
4. a. form hydrogen ions when dissolved in water; have pH values below 7
   b. form hydroxide ions when dissolved in water; have pH values above 7
   c. water-soluble compounds
5. b

SECTION 2-3: CHEMISTRY OF CELLS

1. carbon, hydrogen, and oxygen
2. two atoms of hydrogen to each atom of carbon and oxygen
3. fruits, vegetables, grains
4. monosaccharide; single (one) sugar
5. $C_6H_{12}O_6$; 24 atoms
6. disaccharides; two joined monosaccharides
7. glucose and fructose
8. polysaccharides; three or more monosaccharides joined in a chain
9. d

SECTION 2-4: ENERGY AND CHEMICAL REACTIONS

1. A *substrate* is a substance on which an enzyme acts. *Active sites* are pockets on an enzyme's surface into which the enzyme's substrate fits.
2. starch
3. its shape
4. a. The substrate is attaching to an enzyme's active site.
   b. The enzyme reduces the activation energy of the reaction.
   c. Products form, signaling that the reaction is complete.
5. a

CHAPTER 3
Cell Structure

SECTION 3-1: LOOKING AT CELLS

1. SI is the abbreviation for the International System of Measurements which is the official name of the metric system.
2. SI is a decimal system.
3. the SI unit of length, or the meter, to express the length of objects
4. to indicate the relationship of that unit to a base unit
5. **a.** *Kilo-*
   b. 1,000 m
   c. *Centi-*
   d. 0.01 m
   e. *Milli-*
   f. 0.001
   g. *Micro-*
   h. 0.000001
6. c

SECTION 3-2: CELL FEATURES

1. The middle part of the membrane protein is attracted to the interior of the lipid bilayer but is repelled by the water on either side of the lipid bilayer.
2. The inner and outer parts of the membrane protein are attracted to water.
3. the dual attraction of the inner and outer parts of the protein to water
4. Cause: Phospholipids are fluid and in motion. Effect: Cell-membrane proteins move within the lipid bilayer.
5. that there are different types of proteins in the cell membrane
6. **a.** marker proteins
   b. help other cells recognize their cell type
   c. receptor proteins
   d. recognize and bind to specific substances outside the cell
   e. transport proteins
   f. aid the movement of substances into and out of the cell
7. d

SECTION 3-3: CELL ORGANELLES

1. Golgi apparatus: set of flattened, membrane-bound sacs that serve as the packaging and distribution center of the cell; lysosomes: small, spherical organelles that contain a cell's digestive enzymes
2. The vesicles move from the ER through the cytosol to the Golgi apparatus.
3. From buds on the surface of the Golgi apparatus.
4. proteins, nucleic acids, lipids, and carbohydrates
5. b

CHAPTER 4
Cells and Their Environment

SECTION 4-1: PASSIVE TRANSPORT

1. osmosis; the diffusion of water through a selectively permeable membrane
2. Osmosis is a type of diffusion.
3. Other forms of diffusion involve movement of different substances down a concentration gradient.
4. d

SECTION 4-2: ACTIVE TRANSPORT

1. **a.** movement into cell
   b. movement out of cell
   c. Cell membrane forms pouch around substances outside of cell or; vesicles may fuse with lysosomes or other organelles.
   d. Cell membrane fuses with vesicles in the cell or; cells export proteins that are modified by the Golgi apparatus
2. The prefix indicates that something is occurring inside or within an object. In this case, a vesicle is moving a substance inside, or within a cell.
3. b

CHAPTER 5
Photosynthesis and Cellular Respiration

SECTION 5-1: ENERGY AND LIVING THINGS

1. a putting together of substances, including substances found in light energy, to form chemical energy
2. capable of producing organic compounds, or food, from within itself
3. A heterotroph must obtain organic compounds, or food, by consuming another organism.
4. Possible answers include plants or bacteria. The analogy identifies a classification group and a specific member of that group.
5. Through cellular respiration, the human body gets energy from food. This energy is needed for an organism to carry out its life processes.
6. d

SECTION 5-2: PHOTOSYNTHESIS

1. Photosynthesis is directly affected by various environmental factors.
2. A decrease in light intensity would cause a similar decrease in the photosynthesis level of the plant.
3. Once the light saturation point is reached, light intensity has minimal effect on the photosynthesis level of a plant.

4. The concentration of carbon dioxide steadily increased during the study, causing an increased rate. At the point when the rate leveled off, the carbon dioxide concentration had reached its maximum point.

5. Air temperature dropped to a point at which plant enzymes involved in photosynthesis could not operate properly.

6. b

SECTION 5-3: CELLULAR RESPIRATION

1. Glycolysis occurs in the cytosol of a cell.

2. Glycolysis is not dependent upon the presence of oxygen.

3. It is broken down to form two three-carbon molecules of pyruvate.

4. The energy comes from stored energy in the glucose molecule.

5. d

CHAPTER 6
Chromosomes and Cell Reproduction

SECTION 6-1: CHROMOSOMES

1. A gene is a segment of DNA that codes for a protein or RNA molecule.

2. The strand is stretched out so that the information it contains can be decoded and used to direct the synthesis of proteins needed by the cell.

3. Chromatids are exact copies of DNA that make up chromosomes.

4. b

SECTION 6-2: THE CELL CYCLE

1. cell cycle; interphase

2. cell cycle; repeating sequence of growth and division during the life of a cell, interphase; first three phases of the cell cycle

3. It is about to divide.

4. a. 4
   b. 1
   c. 5
   d. 3
   e. 1
   f. 4
   g. 2
   h. 3
   i. 2
   j. 1
   k. 4

5. Both are phases of the cell cycle in which a cell part divides. However, during mitosis, a nucleus divides, while during cytokinesis, cytoplasm divides.

6. d

SECTION 6-3: MITOSIS AND CYTOKINESIS

1. a. P
   b. B
   c. A
   d. P
   e. B
   f. P

2. d

CHAPTER 7
Meiosis and Sexual Reproduction

SECTION 7-1: MEIOSIS

1. a. TI
   b. PI
   c. AI
   d. MI
   e. PI
   f. TI
   g. AI
   h. PI

2. a. AII
   b. PII
   c. TII
   d. MII
   e. TII
   f. AII
   g. TII

3. a

SECTION 7-2: SEXUAL REPRODUCTION

1. Reproduction, the process of producing offspring, can be asexual or sexual.

2. an organism that is genetically identical to its parent

3. binary fission

4. Because these offspring receive genetic material from both parents, they inherit traits from each.

5. In both processes, offspring are produced.

6. Because asexual production involves a single parent, there is no fusion of haploid cells. Because sexual reproduction involves two parents, haploid cells are joined together.

7. c

CHAPTER 8
Mendel and Heredity

SECTION 8-1: THE ORIGINS OF GENETICS

1. A monohybrid cross involves only one pair of contrasting traits.

2. It provides a specific example of a monohybrid cross.

3. This plant would produce only plants with white flowers.

4. The parental generation is the first two individuals that are crossed in a breeding experiment.

5. the first filial generation or first offspring of the parental generation

6. a. P
   b. F_1
   c. F_2
   d. cross-pollination
   e. self-pollination

7. c

SECTION 8-2: MENDEL'S THEORY

1. by writing the first letter of the trait as a capital letter

2. by writing the first letter of the trait in lowercase

3. Two of the same alleles for seed color are present in the plant.

4. The plant possesses two different alleles for flower color.

5. Yy

6. pp

7. Pp

8. b

SECTION 8-3: STUDYING HEREDITY

1. It defines the Key Term *Punnett square*.

2. They represent the possible gametes produced by each parent.

3. Each combination is formed by taking one allele along the top of the box and one allele along the side of the box.

4. the possible genotypes of offspring produced from these two parents

5. the number of plants expressing either purple flowers or white flowers

6. a. YY
   b. yy
   c. 1
   d. 1
   e. 2
   f. 1
   g. 3

7. d

SECTION 8-4: PATTERNS OF HEREDITY CAN BE COMPLEX

1. It defines the Key Term *multiple alleles*.

2. It clarifies the term *blood groups*, which precedes it.

3. The letters refer to two carbohydrates on the surface of red blood cells.

4. Both I^A and I^B are dominant over the recessive allele i. But neither I^A nor I^B is dominant over the other.

5. Both I^A and I^B are present in the individual. Because they are codominant, the individual shows both forms of the trait.

6. d

CHAPTER 9

DNA: The Genetic Material

SECTION 9-1: IDENTIFYING THE GENETIC MATERIAL

1. It protects the body against future infections by the microorganisms from which it was prepared.

2. The capsule protects the bacterium from the body's defense systems.

3. able to cause disease

4. The mice remained healthy.

5. The mice still lived.

6. The mice died.

7. The live *R* bacteria had acquired polysaccharide capsules.

8. d

SECTION 9-2: THE STRUCTURE OF DNA

1. A double helix consists of two strands twisted around each other.

2. It provides a visual model of a double helix's structure.

3. Answers will vary. Possible responses include a coil of fencing material or railroad tracks that wind around a mountain.

4. Nucleotides are units, or parts, that form DNA, or a whole.

5. a phosphate group, a five-carbon sugar molecule, and a nitrogen base

6. It stands for deoxyribonucleic acid.

7. a

SECTION 9-3: THE REPLICATION OF DNA

1. the process by which a copy of DNA is made

2. during the synthesis (S) phase of the cell cycle before a cell divides

3. the double helix must unwind

4. Part a: The two original DNA strands separate.

   Part b: DNA polymerases add complimentary nucleotides to each strand.

   Part c: When both strands are completely copied, all enzymes detach. Each new and old strand twists to form a double helix.

5. c

CHAPTER 10

Gene Expression

SECTION 10-1: FROM GENES TO PROTEINS

1. a. R   **e.** R
   b. B   **f.** B
   c. D   **g.** D
   d. R   **h.** B

2. c

SECTION 10-2: GENE REGULATION AND STRUCTURE

1. a change in the DNA of a gene
2. Because the mutation was passed to the individual's offspring, the original mutation must have occurred in a gamete.
3. A substitution is a specific type of point mutation in which one nucleotide in a gene is replaced with a different nucleotide.
4. a point mutation in which one or more nucleotides are added to a gene
5. A deletion upsets the triplet groupings, creating a new genetic message.
6. b

CHAPTER 11
Gene Technology

SECTION 11-1: GENETIC ENGINEERING

1. bacterial enzymes that recognize and bind to specific short sequences of DNA
2. an agent that is used to carry the gene of interest into another cell
3. Plasmids are circular DNA molecules that are commonly used as vectors.
4. DNA ligase is an enzyme that is added to DNA fragments to help them bond together.
5. Gene cloning produces many copies of the gene of interest.
6. When bacteria reproduce by binary fission, offspring that are identical to the solitary parent are produced. When a bacterial cell replicates its DNA, it also replicates its plasmid DNA.
7. c

SECTION 11-2: GENETIC ENGINEERING IN MEDICINE AND SOCIETY

1. smallpox and polio
2. a solution containing a harmless version of a pathogen
3. The words *disease-causing microorganism* define the term *pathogen*, which precedes the parentheses.
4. This action is caused by injection of a vaccine into the body.
5. The immune system makes antibodies.
6. The vaccine is prepared either by killing a specific pathogenic microbe or by making the microbe unable to grow.
7. b

SECTION 11-3: GENETIC ENGINEERING IN AGRICULTURE

1. the first successful cloning using differentiated cells from an adult animal
2. a cell that has become specialized to become a specific type of cell
3. It clarifies the term *udder*, which precedes the parentheses.

4. that only embryonic or fetal cells could be cloned and that differentiated cells could not give rise to an entire organism
5. a. 3
   b. 1
   c. 5
   d. 4
   e. 2
6. a

CHAPTER 12
History of Life on Earth

SECTION 12-1: HOW DID LIFE BEGIN?

1. ammonia, methane, and others
2. ultraviolet radiation and lightning
3. complex organic molecules
4. c

SECTION 12-2: COMPLEX ORGANISMS DEVELOP

1. Both are types of prokaryotes.
2. Sulfolobus is a living group of archaebacteria.
3. The cell walls of eubacteria contain peptidoglycan, and their cell membranes contain the same type of lipids found in eukaryotes.
4. The cell walls of archaebacteria lack peptidoglycan, and their cell membranes contain unique lipids.
5. The first bacteria to exist on Earth were closely related to archaebacteria.
6. The first eukaryotic cells likely evolved from archaebacteria.
7. a

SECTION 12-3: LIFE INVADED THE LAND

1. frogs, toads, and salamanders
2. several structural changes in their bodies
3. from the bones of fish fins
4. b

CHAPTER 13
The Theory of Evolution

SECTION 13-1: THE THEORY OF EVOLUTION BY NATURAL SELECTION

1. Malthus believed that while every human has the potential to produce many offspring during his or her lifetime, only a limited number of those offspring survive to further reproduce.
2. observations made on his voyage and his experiences breeding domestic animals
3. Certain individuals have physical or behavioral traits that suit their environment. Because of these traits, the individuals are more likely to survive and reproduce offspring with the same traits. Over time, the number of individuals possessing the traits exceeds the number of individuals lacking the traits, which changes the nature of the population.

4. genes

5. As the number of individuals carrying the alleles for a certain trait increases, the frequency of that trait increases in a population.

6. mutations and recombination of alleles during sexual reproduction

7. d

SECTION 13-2: EVIDENCE OF EVOLUTION

1. a. PE
   b. B
   c. G
   d. B
   e. PE
   f. B
   g. PE
   h. B

2. b

SECTION 13-3: EXAMPLES OF EVOLUTION

1. The title of the graph is "Beak-Size Variation." An observer would expect to discover data regarding differences in the beak size of the members of a certain population.

2. The horizontal axis identifies various years.

3. Each interval on the axis represents 1 year.

4. beak size

5. millimeters

6. Beak size increases.

7. Beak size decreases.

8. c

CHAPTER 14
Human Evolution

SECTION 14-1: THE EVOLUTION OF PRIMATES

1. It notes the time frame when the first primates evolved.

2. a. clawed, unbendable toes
   b. grasping hands and feet
   c. eyes located on sides of the head
   d. eyes positioned at the front of the face

3. a

SECTION 14-2: EARLY HOMINIDS

1. that australopithecines had two key hominid characteristics

2. A hominid that is bipedal is able to walk upright on two legs.

3. it made it difficult for an ape to walk upright for long periods of time

4. it enabled a hominid to be fully bipedal

5. The australopithecine brain had a greater volume, relative to body weight, than that of apes.

6. d

SECTION 14-3: THE GENUS HOMO

1. in Europe about 130,000 years ago

2. The Neanderthal brain was larger.

3. they commonly buried their dead with food, weapons, and even flowers

4. b

CHAPTER 15
Classification of Organisms

SECTION 15-1: CATEGORIES OF BIOLOGICAL CLASSIFICATION

1. form and structure

2. The groups become more and more restrictive, encompassing fewer members who share a greater number of traits.

3. six; Archaebacteria, Eubacteria, Protista, Fungi, Plantae, and Animalia

4. a. Classes
   b. A phylum contains classes.
   c. Orders
   d. A class contains orders.
   e. Families
   f. An order contains families.
   g. Genera
   h. A family contains genera.
   i. A genus contains species.

5. d

SECTION 15-2: HOW BIOLOGISTS CLASSIFY ORGANISMS

1. by inferring relationships based on similarities derived from a common ancestor

2. the sequence in which different groups of organisms evolved

3. Cladistics focuses on derived traits, which are a set of unique characteristics found in a particular group of organisms.

4. the evolutionary relationships that exist among groups of organisms

5. morphological, physiological, molecular, and behavioral traits that differ among the organisms being studied and that can be attributed to a common ancestor

6. c

CHAPTER 16

Populations

SECTION 16-1: HOW POPULATIONS GROW

1. size, density, and dispersion
2. Very small populations are among those most likely to become extinct.
3. the number of individuals that live in a given area
4. When individuals of a population are spread widely apart, they have little opportunity for interactions. This hampers the reproductive capability of the population.
5. a. In a random distribution, the location of each individual is self-determined.
   b. In an even distribution, individuals are located at regular intervals.
   c. In a clumped distribution, individuals are bunched together in clusters.
6. a

SECTION 16-2: HOW POPULATIONS EVOLVE

1. Dominant alleles do not automatically replace recessive alleles.
2. the action of evolutionary forces
3. mutation, gene flow, nonrandom mating, genetic drift, and natural selection
4. can cause the ratios of genotypes to differ significantly
5. Mating with relatives because of small population size causes changes in the frequencies of alleles in that population.
6. d

CHAPTER 17

Ecosystems

SECTION 17-1: WHAT IS AN ECOSYSTEM?

1. a. biotic factors
   b. biodiversity
   c. ecology
   d. community
   e. ecosystem
   f. abiotic factors
   g. habitat
   h. community
   i. ecosystem
2. c

SECTION 17-2: ENERGY FLOW IN ECOSYSTEMS

1. A food chain is the path energy takes as it moves through the trophic levels of an ecosystem.
2. producers
3. herbivores
4. carnivores and omnivores

5. Both omnivores and carnivores eat herbivores. However, omnivores also eat plants.
6. a. 2
   b. 1
   c. 3
   d. 2
   e. 3
   f. 1
   g. 3
   h. 2
7. a

SECTION 17-3: ECOSYSTEMS CYCLE MATERIALS

1. Water vapor in the atmosphere condenses and falls to the Earth's surface as rain or snow.
2. Some becomes groundwater, and the remaining precipitation reenters the atmosphere through evaporation.
3. Water is taken up by the roots of plants.
4. the process by which water moves into the atmosphere through tiny openings in the leaves of plants
5. In order for transpiration to occur, the sun must heat Earth's atmosphere to create the wind currents that draw moisture from plants.
6. a. water vapor
   b. transpiration
   c. evaporation
   d. groundwater
   e. precipitation
7. d

CHAPTER 18

Biological Communities

SECTION 18-1: HOW ORGANISMS INTERACT IN COMMUNITIES

1. a. C
   b. P, M, C
   c. P
   d. C
   e. M, C
2. d

SECTION 18-2: HOW COMPETITION SHAPES COMMUNITIES

1. the first sentence; that Tilman's experiments illustrated the relationship between biodiversity and productivity
2. Tilman monitored plant growth in 147 experimental plots located in a Minnesota prairie.
3. b

SECTION 18-3: MAJOR BIOLOGICAL COMMUNITIES

1. biome
2. tropical rain forest, desert, savanna, temperate deciduous forest, temperate grassland, taiga, and tundra
3. temperature and available moisture decrease
4. d

CHAPTER 19

Human Impact on the Environment

SECTION 19-1: GLOBAL CHANGE

1. Cause: burning of coal in power plants; Effect: release of smoke containing high concentrations of sulfur
2. to release the sulfur-rich smoke high into the atmosphere, where it could be dispersed and diluted by winds
3. It combines with water vapor to produce sulfuric acid.
4. Rain and snow carry the sulfuric acid to Earth's surface.
5. a. 3
   b. 5
   c. 2
   d. 4
   e. 1
6. b

SECTION 19-2: ECOSYSTEM DAMAGE

1. The annual rate of 94 million is an estimated rather than exact figure.
2. Answers will vary based on class time.
3. in the developing countries of Asia, Africa, and Latin America
4. in the industrialized countries of North America, Europe, Japan, New Zealand, and Australia
5. The rate in the United States of 0.8 percent is less than half the global rate. Doubling the U.S. rate yields 1.6 percent, so the world rate must be more than 1.6 percent.
6. a

SECTION 19-3: SOLVING ENVIRONMENTAL PROBLEMS

1. Data is collected and experiments are performed to determine exactly what is happening to the ecosystem.
2. A model makes it possible to describe how the ecosystem is responding to the problem and to predict future events in the ecosystem.
3. explaining the problem in understandable terms, presenting the alternative actions available, and explaining the probable costs and results of different choices
4. by exercising their right to vote and by contacting their elected officials
5. a. 6
   b. 2

c. 7
d. 5
e. 1
f. 4
g. 3
6. d

CHAPTER 20

Introduction to the Kingdoms of Life

SECTION 20-1: SIMPLE UNICELLULAR ORGANISMS

1. the largest taxonomic group of organisms; includes several related phyla
2. Eubacteria, Archaebacteria, Protista, Fungi, Plantae, and Animalia
3. based on their similarities
4. cell type, cell structure, body type, and nutrition of the six kingdoms
5. Protista, Fungi, Plantae, and Animalia
6. Eubacteria, Archaebacteria, Protista, and Fungi
7. Eubacteria, Archaebacteria, Protista, and Plantae
8. Animalia
9. Kingdoms Fungi and Animalia are heterotrophic eukaryotes. While all members of kingdom Animalia are multicellular, only some members of kingdom Fungi are multicellular. In addition, members of kingdom Animalia lack a cell wall while members of kingdom Fungi have a cell wall made of chitin.
10. Members of both kingdom Archaebacteria and Plantae have cell walls. However, members of kingdom Archaebacteria are unicellular prokaryotes that can be either autotrophs or heterotrophs. Members of kingdom Plantae are autotrophic, multicellular eukaryotes.
11. d

SECTION 20-2: ADVENT OF MULTICELLULARITY

1. a group of cells that are permanently associated but do not communicate with each other
2. Because few cell activities are coordinated through the three-dimensional formation, the cyanobacteria are not considered multicellular.
3. c

SECTION 20-3: KINGDOMS OF PLANTS AND ANIMALS

1. multicellular, heterotrophs, cells lack a cell wall, cells are organized as tissues, mostly diploid, and zygotes develop through several stages
2. the presence of muscle, or specialized tissue
3. d

CHAPTER 21
Viruses and Bacteria

SECTION 21-1: VIRUSES

1. After the virus enters a cell, it replicates several hundred times and breaks out, destroying the cell.
2. Viruses are types of pathogens, or agents that cause disease.
3. The cycle of viral infection, replication, and cell destruction is called the lytic cycle.
4. a. The virus attaches to a cell and injects DNA.
   b. Viral DNA enters the lytic cycle or lysogenic cycle.
   c. New viruses are made.
   d. The cell breaks open and releases viruses.
   e. The provirus may enter the lytic cycle.
5. b

SECTION 21-2: BACTERIA

1. a. B
   b. B
   c. E
   d. E
   e. B
   f. E
   g. B
   h. B
   i. E
   j. B
   k. B
   l. E
   m. E
   n. E
   o. B
   p. B
   q. B
   r. E
   s. B
   t. B
2. c

CHAPTER 22
Protists

SECTION 22-1: CHARACTERISTICS OF PROTISTS

1. both sexually and asexually
2. When they reproduce asexually, members of the *Chlamydomonas* species divide by mitosis, producing haploid zoospores.
3. environmental stress such as a shortage of nutrients
4. Haploid gametes released from different *Chlamydomonas* individuals fuse to form a pair. The members of this pair shed their cell walls and fuse to form a diploid zygote.
5. a. mature cell
   b. zoospores
   c. mitosis
   d. gametes
   e. zygote
   f. meiosis
   g. mitosis
6. d

SECTION 22-2: PROTIST DIVERSITY

1. amoeba; protists that move using flexible, cytoplasmic extensions
2. The Greek word *pseudo* means "false," and *podium* means "foot." Combining these words produces the Key Term *pseudopodium* which means "false foot."
3. Because an amoeba lacks cells walls and flagella, it is extremely flexible.
4. b

SECTION 22-3: PROTISTS AND HEALTH

1. a. As an infected mosquito bites a human, it injects a chemical that prevents blood from clotting. It also injects protists with its saliva. Sporozoites infect the liver and divide rapidly.
   b. Merozoites produced in the liver infect red blood cells and divide rapidly. The blood cells rupture, releasing more merozoites and toxic substances. Every 48 to 72 hours, new waves of blood cells are infected and destroyed.
   c. Merozoites in the blood develop into gametes. After these gametes are eaten by a mosquito, they form a zygote. Infectious sporozoites are formed in the zygote and migrate to the salivary glands of the mosquito. The malaria parasite matures in the mosquito before infecting another human.
2. a

CHAPTER 23
Fungi

SECTION 23-1: CHARACTERISTICS OF FUNGI

1. because both groups of organisms are immobile, have a cell wall, and appear "rooted" in the soil
2. A mushroom, like other fungi, lacks chlorophyll. Plants contain this pigment, which gives a plant its green coloring.
3. by breaking down organic molecules that they absorb from their environment
4. In most eukaryotes, the nuclear envelope disintegrates in prophase and reforms in telophase. In fungi, the nuclear envelope remains intact from prophase to anaphase.
5. a. F   f. B
   b. F   g. P
   c. B   h. P
   d. P   i. B
   e. F   j. F
6. b

SECTION 23-2: FUNGAL DIVERSITY

1. **a.** 4
   b. 5
   c. 1
   d. 4
   e. 3
2. b

SECTION 23-3: FUNGAL PARTNERSHIPS

1. **a.** Effect: The photosynthetic partner can carry out photosynthesis.
   b. Cause: The fungus has a sturdy structure and the alga can carry out photosynthesis.
2. d

CHAPTER 24
Introduction to Plants

SECTION 24-1: ADAPTATIONS OF PLANTS

1. seed or seed plant; a structure that contains a plant embryo
2. It protects an embryo from drying out, from sustaining mechanical injury, and from contracting disease
3. from the supply of organic nutrients stored in the seed that surrounds it
4. The meaning, *spread*, is placed within parentheses after the word.
5. by wind, water, or animals
6. water, nutrients, light, and living space
7. **a.** wing
   b. seed coat
   c. warm weather
   d. moisture
8. a

SECTION 24-2: KINDS OF PLANTS

1. **a.** L
   b. M
   c. L, H
   d. M
   e. M, H
   f. M, L
   g. L
   h. M
   i. H
   j. M, L, H
   k. M
   l. H
   m. M
   n. M, H
   o. L
   p. L
2. d

SECTION 24-3: PLANTS IN OUR LIVES

1. The first sentence is the topic sentence, which expresses the main idea of this passage.

2. *cereals* and *grain*; Cereals are grasses that are grown as food for humans and livestock. A grain is a type of dry, edible fruit.
3. a single seed with a large supply of endosperm; it is covered by a dry, papery husk called the bran, which includes the wall of the ovary and the seed coat.
4. b

CHAPTER 25
Plant Reproduction

SECTION 25-1: SEXUAL REPRODUCTION IN SEEDLESS PLANTS

1. Through meiosis, a diploid sporophyte produces spores.
2. Through mitosis, fern gametophytes produce gametes.
3. sperm can swim to archegonia and fertilize the eggs inside them
4. **a.** 4
   b. 2
   c. 5
   d. 1
   e. 3
5. **a.** adult sporophyte
   b. spores
   c. mature gametophyte
   d. mitosis
   e. archegonium
   f. fertilization
   g. zygote
   h. sporangium
6. c

SECTION 25-2: SEXUAL REPRODUCTION IN SEED PLANTS

1. in four concentric whorls
2. protect the flower from damage while it is a bud
3. attract pollinators to the flower
4. An anther is a pollen-producing sac located at the tip of a stamen.
5. a

SECTION 25-3: ASEXUAL REPRODUCTION

1. growing new plants from seed or vegetative parts
2. grafting, taking cuttings, and tissue culture
3. a description of each method as well as examples of plants commonly produced by each type of vegetative plant propagation
4. Small stems from one plant are attached to larger stems or roots of another plant.
5. African violets, ornamental trees and shrubs, and figs
6. b

CHAPTER 26
Plant Structure and Function

SECTION 26-1: THE VASCULAR PLANT BODY

1. from the Greek words *epi*, meaning "upon," and *dermis*, meaning "skin"
2. prevents water loss
3. helps slow water loss, while those found on root tips increase water absorption
4. several layers of dead cells that make up the dermal tissue on woody stems and roots
5. protects the plant body, aids in gas exchange and the absorption of mineral nutrients
6. c

SECTION 26-2: TRANSPORT IN PLANTS

1. a. Cause: Water pressure changes.
   b. Effect: The guard cells swell.
   c. Cause: The cell walls of guard cells contain extra cellulose.
   d. Effect: The stoma opens.
   e. Cause: Water leaves the guard cells.
   f. Effect: Transpiration stops.
2. a. A stoma opens as the guard cells take in water, lengthen, and move apart.
   b. A stoma closes as the guard cells lose water, shorten, and come together.
3. b

CHAPTER 27
Plant Growth and Development

SECTION 27-1: HOW PLANTS GROW AND DEVELOP

1. a. A
   b. P
   c. B
   d. P
   e. A
2. d

SECTION 27-2: REGULATING PLANT GROWTH AND DEVELOPMENT

1. a response, or change, due to touch
2. a response, or change, due to light
3. Auxins are responsible for producing tropisms.
4. Both positive and negative tropisms are responses to a stimulus. If the response is toward the stimulus, then it is classified as a positive tropism. If the response is away from the stimulus, then it is classified as a negative tropism.
5. a

CHAPTER 28
Introduction to Animals

SECTION 28-1: ANIMALS—FEATURES AND BODY PLANS

1. a type of branching diagram that shows how animals are related through evolution
2. Scientists study the fossil record, compare the anatomy and physiology of living animals, compare patterns of development in animal embryos, and compare the DNA in the genes of various animal species.
3. d

SECTION 28-2: ANIMAL BODY SYSTEMS

1. a. B
   b. S
   c. A
   d. B
   e. S
   f. A
2. b

CHAPTER 29
Simple Invertebrates

SECTION 29-1: SPONGES

1. gemmules; Gemmules are clusters of amoebocytes encased in protective coats that can become new organisms.
2. Sponges can reproduce asexually by regeneration, budding, and by forming gemmules.
3. Cause: A piece of a sponge breaks away from the main body of the organism.
   Effect: A new sponge develops.
4. Cause: Living conditions become harsh.
   Effect: Freshwater sponges form gemmules.
5. Cause: A gemmule contains a supply of food.
   Effect: The amoebocytes survive.
6. Cause: Harsh environmental conditions subside.
   Effect: Amoebocytes develop into new organisms.
7. a

SECTION 29-2: CNIDARIANS

1. a. medusa
   b. polyp
   c. ectoderm
   d. endoderm
   e. tentacle
   f. mouth
2. c

SECTION 29-3: FLATWORMS AND ROUNDWORMS

1. It serves to protect the animal and give shape to its body.
2. skin protects body; skeletal system protects inner organs, shapes body
3. They are microscopic, free-living, active hunters.
4. b

CHAPTER 30
Mollusks and Annelids

SECTION 30-1: MOLLUSKS

1. **a.** mantle
   b. mantle cavity
   c. visceral mass
   d. foot
2. foot
3. visceral mass
4. mantle
5. a

SECTION 30-2: ANNELIDS

1. digestive, excretory, and locomotor
2. It provides information about the meaning of the word that precedes it—locomotor.
3. reproduction, feeding, or sensation
4. b

CHAPTER 31
Arthropods

SECTION 31-1: FEATURES OF ARTHROPODS

1. a skeleton found outside an organism's body.
2. protects the organism from predators and helps prevent water loss
3. ecdysis
4. b

SECTION 31-2: SPIDERS AND OTHER ARACHNIDS

1. a cephalothorax and an abdomen
2. six; one pair of chelicerae, one pair of pedipalps, and four pairs of walking legs
3. to catch and handle prey
4. d

SECTION 31-3: INSECTS AND THEIR RELATIVES

1. **a.** C
   b. B
   c. I
   d. B
   e. C
   f. B
   g. I
   h. C
   i. C
   j. I
2. b

SECTION 31-4: CRUSTACEANS

1. Great numbers of crustaceans inhabit the world's oceans just as insects dominate the world's land areas.
2. ocean dwellers; also found in freshwater and terrestrial habitats
3. the distinctive larval form of crustaceans; a series of molts
4. **a.** Crustaceans have two pairs of antennae.
   b. Insects have one pair of antennae.
   c. Crustaceans have gills for respiration.
   d. Insects have a tracheal system.
   e. The walking legs of a crustacean are attached to both the thorax and abdomen.
   f. The walking legs of an insect are attached only to the thorax.
5. a

CHAPTER 32
Echinoderms and Invertebrate Chordates

SECTION 32-1: ECHINODERMS

1. an opening that leads to the outside of a gastrula
2. the mouth
3. Echinodermata and Chordata
4. The word part *protos* means "first" and *stoma* means "mouth." Combining these meanings yields "first mouth," which indicates that protosomes first develop a mouth from or near the blastopore.
5. The word part *deutero-* means "second" and *stoma* means "mouth." Combining these meanings yields "second mouth," which indicates that deuterostomes develop a mouth second. They first develop an anus from or near the blastopore.
6. **a.** protostome
   b. deuterostome
   c. gut
   d. coelum
   e. blastopore
   f. coelum
   g. gut
   h. blastopore
7. a

SECTION 32-2: INVERTEBRATE CHORDATES

1. An endoskeleton that is completely internal or inside the organism.
2. The endoskeleton made it possible for animals to grow large and move quickly.
3. in the wall of the pharynx
4. As embryos, all chordates develop a notochord along their backs.
5. a

CHAPTER 33
Introduction to Vertebrates

SECTION 33-1: VERTEBRATES SPREAD FROM THE SEA TO THE LAND

1. provides support for the dorsal nerve cord, protects the dorsal nerve cord, and provides a site for muscle attachment
2. d

SECTION 33-2: VERTEBRATES ADAPT TO TERRESTRIAL LIVING

1. The word parts provide information to the meaning of each Key Term.
2. to produce enough heat to warm their bodies
3. They produce heat internally because of their quick metabolism.
4. a

CHAPTER 34
Fishes and Amphibians

SECTION 34-1: THE FISH BODY

1. to force the water from the mouth, over the gills, and out through the gill slits
2. A gill is made up of rows of gill slits.
3. Countercurrent flow ensures that oxygen diffuses into the blood over the entire length of the capillaries in the gills.
4. a

SECTION 34-2: TODAY'S FISHES

1. a gill cover, a lateral line system, and a swim bladder
2. a hard plate that covers the gills of most bony fishes
3. helps the bony fish conserve energy that can then be spent chasing after prey and escaping from predators
4. a specialized sensory system that extends along each side of a bony fish's body
5. makes it possible for a bony fish to perceive its position and rate of movement and detect a motionless object
6. a special gas sac that enables a bony fish to regulate its buoyancy
7. Because the swim bladders of early bony fishes were connected to their throats, the fishes could gulp air to fill the gas sac.
8. c

SECTION 34-3: AMPHIBIANS

1. Caecilians lost their legs during the evolutionary course of adapting to a burrowing existence.
2. Pulmonary veins deliver oxygen-rich blood from the lungs to the heart. The heart then pumps the blood, at a higher pressure than when it left the lungs, to all body tissues.
3. is respiring through the skin

4. Cutaneous respiration is only efficient when there is a high ratio of skin surface to body volume.
5. d

CHAPTER 35
Reptiles and Birds

SECTION 35-1: THE REPTILIAN BODY

1. a. Effect: A reptile's body temperature is largely determined by the temperature of its environment.
   b. Effect: The reptile's body temperature increases.
   c. Effect: The lizard maintains a relatively constant body temperature.
2. a

SECTION 35-2: TODAY'S REPTILES

1. Other reptiles lack the protective shell that encases the body of a turtle or tortoise.
2. No, the shells of most tortoises are dome-shaped, while most water-dwelling turtles have a streamlined, disk-shaped shell.
3. d

SECTION 35-3: CHARACTERISTICS AND DIVERSITY OF BIRDS

1. Because of one-way air flow, the lungs are exposed to almost fully oxygenated air which increases the amount of oxygen transported to body cells; because the flow of blood in the lungs runs in a different direction than the flow of air, oxygen absorption increases.
2. c

CHAPTER 36
Mammals

SECTION 36-1: THE MAMMALIAN BODY

1. dead cells filled with the protein keratin; mammals
2. insulation
3. Since mammals typically maintain body temperatures higher than the temperature of their surroundings, they tend to lose body heat.
4. protective coloration; a clear signal to predators; a sensory structure; a defensive weapon
5. b

SECTION 36-2: TODAY'S MAMMALS

1. kangaroos, opossums, wombats, wallaro, and koala
2. Since almost all marsupial species are found in the Australian region, a study site in Australia, New Guinea, or a nearby island would be a logical location.
3. The break up of Pangaea about 70 million years ago caused the Australian region to separate from the continents of Antarctica

and South America. At the time of this separation, placental mammals had not yet reached the Australian region. As a result, the marsupials there developed in isolation.

4. d

CHAPTER 37
Animal Behavior

SECTION 37-1: EVOLUTION OF BEHAVIOR

1. genes and experience
2. genetically programmed behavior or instinct
3. because the spider builds her web exactly the same way every time
4. In many animals, learning is very important in determining the final nature of innate behavior.
5. a type of learning in which the animal learns to ignore a frequent, harmless stimulus
6. c

SECTION 37-2: TYPES OF BEHAVIOR

1. Many primates have a vocabulary of sounds that allows individuals to communicate the identity of specific predators.
2. They are physically unable to produce the sounds of speech.
3. b

CHAPTER 38
Introduction to Body Structure

SECTION 38-1: BODY ORGANIZATION

1. Connective tissue cells in bone are densely packed, while those found in blood are spaced apart from each other.
2. The actions of voluntary muscle can be controlled, while those of involuntary muscle cannot be consciously controlled.
3. a. Smooth muscle
   b. Nerve tissue
   c. Skeletal muscle
   d. Epithelial tissue
   e. Connective tissue
   f. Cardiac muscle
   g. Epithelial tissue
   h. Connective tissue
   i. Epithelial tissue
   j. Nervous tissue
   k. Cardiac muscle
4. d

SECTION 38-2: SKELETAL SYSTEM

1. red bone marrow
2. mostly of fat
3. nutrients
4. a. bone marrow
   b. spongy bone
   c. compact bone
   d. periosteum

5. a. This dense connective tissue forms the hard outer shell of a bone.
   b. This loosely structured network of separated connective tissue forms a bone's porous inner core.
6. b

SECTION 38-3: MUSCULAR SYSTEM

1. The connective tissue holds muscle cells together and provides elasticity.
2. Actin and myosin are both protein filaments that enable muscles to contract.
3. They trigger a specific response by muscle tissue.
4. A sarcomere contains actin and myosin.
5. a. Z line
   b. Myofibril
   c. Myosin
   d. Actin
   e. Sarcomere
6. a. thin protein filaments found in muscle tissue that enable muscles to contract
   b. small cylindrical structures that form a muscle fiber
   c. thick protein filaments found in muscle tissue that enable muscles to contract
   d. area between two Z lines which contains overlapping protein filaments that interact with one another
   e. center of each light-colored band of a myofibril that anchors actin filaments
7. d

SECTION 38-4: SKIN, HAIR, AND NAILS

1. acne; a chronic inflammatory condition that involves the skin's oil-producing glands
2. sebum; an oily secretion that lubricates the skin
3. pores
4. a

CHAPTER 39
Circulatory and Respiratory Systems

SECTION 39-1: THE CIRCULATORY SYSTEM

1. Blood circulates through the body through a network of vessels.
2. By breaking down the term into its word parts, you would determine that an arteriole is a "small" or "little" artery.
3. Capillaries are tiny blood vessels that allow the exchange of gas, nutrients, hormones, and other molecules traveling in blood.
4. arteries, arterioles, capillaries, venules, and veins
5. These elastic fibers enable the blood vessel to expand to accommodate a pulse of blood ejected into the artery from the heart.

6. a. artery
   b. vein
   c. connective tissue
   d. smooth muscle
   e. arterioles
   f. capillaries
   g. venules

7. b

SECTION 39-2: THE HEART

1. the condition of the person's arteries; useful in diagnosing high blood pressure and hardening of the arteries

2. Systolic pressure measures this force as blood flows through arteries when the heart contracts, while diastolic pressure measures this force when the heart relaxes.

3. d

SECTION 39-3: THE RESPIRATORY SYSTEM

1. gas exchange

2. Oxygen gas is a component of air, making up about 21 percent of the air taken into the respiratory system.

3. The epiglottis is a flap of tissue that covers the opening to the larynx, and prevents food and liquids from passing into the lungs.

4. between the alveoli and surrounding capillaries

5. a. pharynx
   b. larynx
   c. trachea
   d. lung
   e. bronchi
   f. bronchioles
   g. capillaries
   h. alveoli

6. c

CHAPTER 40
Digestive and Excretory Systems

SECTION 40-1: YOUR BODY'S NEED FOR FOOD

1. age, sex, rate of growth, and level of physical activity

2. substances needed by the body for energy, growth, repair, and maintenance

3. carbohydrates, lipids, proteins, vitamins, and minerals

4. water

5. the breaking down of food into molecules the body can use

6. Some nutrients must be changed into smaller molecules in order to be absorbed into the blood and carried to cells throughout the body.

7. When cells break these chemical bonds, energy is released.

8. Cells use the energy to make ATP during cellular respiration.

9. Both are units used to measure the amount of energy available in food; they differ in that one Calorie is equal to 1,000 calories.

10. c

SECTION 40-2: DIGESTION

1. the digestion and absorption of nutrients

2. The diameter of the small intestine is relatively small when compared with the diameter of the large intestine.

3. The duodenum is actually the first part of the small intestine.

4. pancreas, liver, and gallbladder

5. These digestive enzymes are involved in the digestion of carbohydrates into monosaccharides, proteins into amino acids, and lipids into fatty acids and glycerol.

6. pancreatic enzymes that digest fats

7. Bile breaks up fat globules into tiny fat droplets.

8. Bile is stored in the gall bladder until it is needed in the small intestine.

9. Villi are fingerlike projections that line the small intestine. Microvilli are projections located on the cells covering each villus.

10. b

SECTION 40-3: EXCRETION

1. cellular respiration and the metabolism of proteins and nucleic acids

2. by either excreting or conserving salts and water

3. the process that rids the body of toxic chemicals and maintains osmotic and pH balance

4. c

CHAPTER 41
The Body's Defenses

SECTION 41-1: NONSPECIFIC DEFENSES

1. the inflammatory response; the temperature response; producing proteins that kill or inhibit pathogens; by sending white blood cells to attack and kill the pathogens

2. a series of events that suppress infection and speed recovery

3. Increased blood flow serves to bring white blood cells to the infected area, causes swelling in the area, and causes redness in the area.

4. Fever slows the growth of certain bacteria that do not grow well at high temperatures.

5. **Part a:** Pathogens invade the body through a puncture in the skin.

   Part b: The release of histamine causes increased blood flow to the area, which triggers swelling and redness.

   Part c: White blood cells attack and destroy the invading pathogens.

6. d

SECTION 41-2: IMMUNE RESPONSE

1. **a.** B cells
   b. macrophages
   c. cytotoxic T cells
   d. helper T cells
   e. macrophages
   f. helper T cells

2. b; (divide 100 by 2)

SECTION 41-3: DISEASE TRANSMISSION AND PREVENTION

1. Because the second animal did not become ill, the injected pathogen does not cause the disease.

2. d

SECTION 41-4: DISORDERS OF THE IMMUNE SYSTEM

1. HIV is most commonly transmitted through sexual contact.

2. Because semen, vaginal fluid, and mucous membranes can contain HIV, either males or females can become infected.

3. HIV can be passed between drug users who share a hypodermic needle stained with HIV-infected blood.

4. Today, blood made available for transfusions is tested for HIV.

5. Because HIV or infected cells cannot survive in air, they cannot be transmitted through this medium.

6. a

CHAPTER 42
Nervous System

SECTION 42-1: NEURONS AND NERVE IMPULSES

1. by transmitting nerve impulses to body tissues and organs, including muscles, glands, and other neurons

2. Dendrites receive information from other cells.

3. collects information from dendrites, relays this information to other parts of the neuron, and maintains the general functioning of the neuron

4. a long extension of the cytoplasm that conducts nerve impulses

5. Nerves contain the axons of many different neurons.

6. c

SECTION 42-2: STRUCTURES OF THE NERVOUS SYSTEM

1. **a.** cerebellum
   b. brain stem
   c. cerebrum
   d. cerebrum
   e. brain stem
   f. cerebrum
   g. cerebellum

h. cerebrum
i. brain stem
j. brain stem
k. cerebrum
l. cerebellum
m. cerebrum
n. brain stem
o. cerebellum
p. cerebrum
q. cerebellum
r. brain stem
s. cerebrum

2. d

SECTION 42-3: SENSORY SYSTEMS

1. The ear enables you to hear and helps you maintain your balance.

2. Energy in sound waves is changed to electrical signals in the ear.

3. The tympanic membrane vibrates when sound waves pass through the ear canal and strike the eardrum.

4. a fluid-filled chamber within the inner ear

5. The bones of the middle ear, which are the anvil, hammer, and stirrup, transfer vibrations from the eardrum to the cochlea.

6. The hair cells generate nerve impulses in the auditory nerve.

7. fluid-filled chambers in the inner ear that contain hair cells

8. Hair cells in the semicircular canals respond to changes in head position with respect to gravity. The hair cells generate electrical signals and send these signals to the brain. The brain interprets these signals to determine the orientation and position of the head.

9. d

SECTION 42-4: DRUGS AND THE NERVOUS SYSTEM

1. A depressant is a drug that generally decreases the activity of the central nervous system.

2. Reaction times increase and coordination, judgment, and speech become impaired.

3. Alcohol is absorbed into the blood through the stomach and small intestine.

4. a

CHAPTER 43
Hormones and the Endocrine System

SECTION 43-1: HORMONES

1. The first sentence defines the term *gland*.

2. ductless organs that secrete hormones directly into either the bloodstream or fluid around cells

3. extracellular fluid

4. The brain, stomach, small intestine, kidney, liver, and heart contain cells that secrete hormones.

5. The exocrine part of the pancreas produces digestive enzymes and delivers them to the small intestine through ducts. The endocrine part of the pancreas secretes two hormones into the bloodstream that regulate blood glucose levels.

6. a

SECTION 43-2: HOW HORMONES WORK

1. The hormones are not fat soluble.

2. The shape of the receptor protein changes.

3. an amino-acid-based hormone made in the pancreas

4. a molecule that passes a message from the first messenger, or hormone, to the cell

5. a change in the shape of a receptor protein

6. An enzyme is activated that converts ATP to a second messenger called cyclic AMP.

7. activates or deactivates certain enzymes in a cascading fashion

8. b

SECTION 43-3: THE MAJOR ENDOCRINE GLANDS OF THE BODY

1. Together they serve as a major control center for the rest of the endocrine system.

2. The area of the brain that coordinates the activities of the nervous and endocrine systems.

3. temperature, blood pressure, and emotions

4. through signals sent from the nervous system as well as from blood concentrations of circulating hormones

5. by producing hormones that provide response instructions to the pituitary gland

6. suspended from the hypothalamus by a short stalk

7. Both releasing and inhibiting hormones are produced by nerve cells in the hypothalamus and released into a special network of blood vessels between the hypothalamus and pituitary gland. Releasing hormones cause the front part of the pituitary gland to make and then release a corresponding pituitary hormone, while inhibiting hormones signal the anterior pituitary gland to stop secreting one of its hormones.

8. c

CHAPTER 44
Reproduction and Development

SECTION 44-1: MALE REPRODUCTIVE SYSTEM

1. explains what occurs through sexual reproduction

2. Males produce sperm cells and deliver the sperm cells to the female reproductive system, in order to fertilize an egg cell.

3. gamete-producing organs of the male reproductive system

4. an external skin sac that contains the testes

5. The testes form inside the abdominal cavity and then move down into the scrotum either before or shortly after birth.

6. The temperature in the scrotum is about 3°C lower than it is in the rest of the body. This is a suitable temperature for sperm to complete development.

7. c

SECTION 44-2: FEMALE REPRODUCTIVE SYSTEM

1. about every 28 days

2. a passageway through which an ovum moves from an ovary toward the uterus

3. rhythmic contractions of smooth muscles that line a fallopian tube

4. a

SECTION 44-3: DEVELOPMENT

1. a. 5
   b. 3
   c. 6
   d. 2
   e. 4
   f. 7
   g. 1

2. a fallopian tube

3. a diploid cell called a zygote

4. b

SECTION 44-4: SEXUALLY TRANSMITTED DISEASES

1. Because viruses—which cause STDs—are not affected by antibiotics, viral STDs cannot be treated by such medications.

2. Both AIDS and genital herpes are transmitted through sexual contact.

3. a